C0-EES-790

ONE OF MY SONS came home from school one day and announced proudly that he'd been in a play. It was about a bullfight.

"You should see my costume!" he cried. "Spanish! And is it fancy!"

"What do you do?"

"Boy, you should see it. Some of the kids are matadors and some of the kids are bulls and they run around and chase each other and everything."

"What do *you* do?"

"Who me? Oh, I don't *do* anything. I just stand there in all my splendor and *observe*."

Well, in a sense, that is what I've done in this little book. Observed other people "running around and everything." Many of them got into the stories that are included. And, life being what it is, inevitably I got into the act.

Ethel Barrett

THERE I STOOD
IN ALL MY SPLENDOR

... Eight vignettes of life. Some of them will make you laugh. Some of them will make you cry. Some of them will make you pray. But all of them will make you think.

THERE I STOOD IN ALL MY SPLENDOR

BY ETHEL BARRETT

G/L REGAL BOOKS

A DIVISION OF G/L PUBLICATIONS
Glendale, California 91205 USA

Second Printing, 1967
Third Printing, 1968
Fourth Printing, 1970
Fifth Printing, 1971

© Copyright 1966 G/L Publications
All rights reserved

Printed in U.S.A.

Published by
REGAL BOOKS DIVISION, G/L PUBLICATIONS
Glendale, California 91209, U.S.A.

*To Melissa, Mike and Sean—
who remind me
that time is still marching on . . .*

CONTENTS

Chapter		
1	Life with Mother	1
2	Mask	28
3	Children Are Not Defenseless	57
4	Time	83
5	A Merry Heart	102
6	Broken Swords	129
7	Death Is a Private Affair	157
8	Time Marches On	186
	Epilogue	213

The stories contained in these chapters were originally radio scripts. They have been rewritten as stories for easier reading.

CHAPTER 1

LIFE WITH MOTHER

Life with mother was both peaceful and exciting—solemn with responsibility and hilarious with fun—serious about the serious things of God and joyful about His goodness. She was both mother and father to us all. It was not until years later when I was both mother and father to my sons that I realized she must have had moments of doubting her own adequacy—and moments of loneliness and panic...

But she always made us feel that we were fortunate and rich—and now as I look back, indeed we were....

Now nobody can be summed up in one sentence. The complexities in our make-up render it quite impossible. But people are constantly being summed up in one sentence, none the less, and we take it as a matter of course, knowing that the summation is a long-range view. With all our inconsistencies we emerge after a few years with general behavior patterns and we are bound to be more or less consistent in some things.

If I were to sum up my mother in one sentence according to the over-all impression she has left on me—I would say that she was a happy woman. Now I'll admit that this is no earth-shaking statement to make, like "My mother was a skin-diver" or "My mother was a secret service agent." It becomes significant only in the face of the fact that from a human standpoint she had very little to be happy about. For some strange reason she never seemed to get hold of this fact, and not only went right on being happy anyway, but managed to keep the rest of us from realizing that we had nothing to be happy about either. This is no mean feat, and bears some analysis, so at the risk of indulging in what might be cloyingly familiar and sentimental terminology, I'm going to evoke a bit of the past to try to explain what her secret might have been.

"We" were a miscellaneous collection of driftwood —my sister and myself, an assortment of orphan cousins, male and female, who came and went periodically—and my grandmother who took care of us all while mother worked. I was told that my father was handsome (his picture bore that out), attended Syracuse University, was a hero, and was buried in Flanders Field. I was shown his medals. But it was all done with pride and not with tears.

None of us knew we were unfortunate. Mother sewed late into the evenings, and from under her magic fingers emerged clothing for all of us—shirts and jackets for the boys, and dresses and coats for the girls—and extensive and imaginative wardrobes for the dolls from the leftover scraps. There was plenty to eat, and as far as we knew, we were rich.

She could work all day, make fudge and popcorn balls in the evening, adjust the crystal set earphones and listen to a radio play while the washing machine was churning away in the summer kitchen, march us off to bed and hear our prayers, sew late into the night, hang out the laundry early next morning—and be off to work again, her lunch in a paper bag. She was indefatigable—if not physically, certainly in attitude.

We lived in many places in my early childhood—and every place was pretty, scrubbed and painted to a standstill inside and gardened and raked and trimmed outside. My mother loved flowers. She talked to them, encouraged them to grow, complimented them on their progress and beauty, and apologized to them when she had to throw a bowl of dead ones out. They grew for her with a fanatical and impassioned zeal, like a dedicated and inspired team that goes all out for a great coach.

When we start to dredge the morass of memory, all sorts of things come up—some of them dangerous contraband, some of them gems. My dredging produces mostly gems, and one of the most rib-tickling ones is a Model T Ford that we called (with a singular lack of imagination) Henry.

It was when we lived on my uncle's farm that mother bought Henry. We had gone there to tide us over a city-housing shortage crisis, though she had made it seem like a lark. We lived in several rooms over a huge carriage house. The place had been converted and had a studio-like atmosphere that would probably be considered quite charming and artistic today. It was different from our city houses and we thought it fun, especially so because from its upper windows we had a view of the entire farm, the surrounding meadows which boasted a huge pond, and the city way in the distance in the valley. From these windows we could also watch for mother at dinner time, alighting from her "ride" home from work, way out by the mailbox. We would scramble to meet her, telling her of the day's triumphs and troubles, and asking her to be mediator in all the unresolved spats of the day. If the ratio of spats was high, she would laugh and say, "Wait till I've had a cup of tea. We'll all feel better after dinner." It always worked. After dinner we'd either forgotten all about it, or the edge was gone.

But this particular night her "ride" went right past the mailbox, and while we were still speculating on what had become of mother, she came driving along in a Model T, and careened around the corner by the mailbox without benefit of slowing down. The Ford literally shot into the lane, its thin tires alternately descending into and bouncing out of the deep ruts, and plunged into the huge area between the main house and the barns, but it didn't stop there. It continued at the same speed toward the corncrib and we got a blurred image of mother determinedly steering, her mouth set in grim lines. All she had to do of course was turn off the ignition and all the fuss would be over in a minute, but for some strange reason this did not occur to any of us. The Ford was an unleashed monster by now. It plowed between the corncrib and the barn, neatly nicked off a corner of the pig pen, sending boards and splinters askew—and shot with wild abandon down into the alfalfa field. By that time we were running from all directions—we kids, my aunt and uncle—all but gramma. She stood in the doorway with her apron over her head. Gramma was a Comstock, from *the* Comstocks, and she never forgot it even in moments of great stress. Father might have attended Syracuse University but a Comstock had founded it. Comstock women never ran or shouted. They stood still and threw their aprons over their heads and waited until the crisis was past.

Well, down in the middle of the alfalfa field, we found mother, her face a mixture of fury, apology and unbelief. Both hands were still tight on the wheel, one of them clutching the instruction book also. She'd kept it in proximity to look up any salient points of driving she might forget on the trip home; unfortunately it was impossible to drive and look up anything at the same time. This would have worked out very well if she'd forgotten anything else, but she'd forgotten how to stop.

We brushed off the alfalfa, murmuring words of comfort, and then suddenly the ridiculousness of it, and the relief that she was not hurt, hit us all in the same moment and we sat down on the running boards and laughed. As shaken as she was, she laughed with us, and then got out with rubber knees to survey the damage. The encounter with the pig pen had done surprisingly little damage; she had just sort of bounced off.

My uncle, who had already memorized the intricacies of the instruction book from *his* Model T, drove the car back to the carriage house. A couple of startled pigs came squealing out, and sent us scurrying to round up the rest of them. Mother wanted to help, but we protested, prescribing for her, her own infallible remedy for everything. "Take the apron off gramma's head and go get a cup of tea. After dinner you'll feel better." After dinner she did feel better and, undaunted, got back into the Model T and practiced every conceivable maneuver with my uncle as instructor and insurance against catastrophe. The next morning we gathered in the yard, shouting instructions and encouragement after her as she proudly drove off to work.

In starting a Model T you had to set the spark, the gas and the brake, go around to the front and crank it, then, when the engine turned over, dash madly back to reset the spark and the gas to keep the thing going. In order to expedite this bit of legerdemain, mother taught us what to do, and by turns we would be allowed to sit proudly in the front seat and work the spark and the gas while she cranked. It was a great privilege and honor we all wanted to earn, and mother, always quick to seize an advantage, used it in the threat and reward department.

Of course you never knew when you started out for a ride whether you were going to get back on your own steam or hire a horse. Hills were the greatest threat and whenever we came to one we would steel ourselves to a man. We had some idea that by settling down in our seats we somehow held poor Henry back—and when he would begin to show signs of strain, we would all lean forward and strain with him, and as he staggered to a standstill we would propel ourselves forward and backward rhythmically, like galley slaves rowing a boat, until he finally gave up. It never worked but we did it every time. I used to wonder why we didn't cut holes in his floor for just such emergencies, and stick our feet through and crawl up the hill like some giant centipede.

Often little time was consumed actually riding. Most of it was spent playing by a brook or in the fields while mother and my uncle sat wearily on the running board going over the part of the instruction book that told what to do in various emergencies. Gramma would be deposited in the shade of a tree where she waited in stoic silence. She refused to wait in the car for fear it would suddenly start by itself while they were still sitting on the running board, and run off with her. And we were admonished to stay close by in case it started; the object was to all pile in, in the shortest time possible (never *mind* who sits where!) before it quit again. Although our family was filled with explosive individualists, Henry was the greatest diva of all.

It wasn't only blowouts and an unpredictable engine that kept us in an uproar. One night mother came driving home from work in a torrential summer shower, the top collapsed all about her and her head sticking out through the hole it had punctured during the mishap. I don't know what kind of material Model T tops were made of in those days, but her head had gone through with no trouble at all when the top fell upon her. She looked like an enormous ghoulish vampire, black wings outspread, flying low in search of prey. Being a woman of quick decisions and no nonsense, she'd kept right on driving rather than stop and attempt to put the top up again and risk having the engine quit with some strange malady she would be unable to diagnose.

As easy-going and fun-loving as mother was, when it came to dealing out punishment she was something to reckon with. We had certain boundaries on the farm. It was filled with expensive and dangerous equipment and choice fruit to be sold, and anyone who went off bounds was promptly dealt with. There was one group of apple trees we were absolutely forbidden to touch. Apples on the ground, yes. But they had better be apples that fell unaided, by their own choice. And climbing the trees was the most flagrant of all crimes. But those apples were the best tasting on the whole farm—indeed in the whole world—and one tree was only fifty feet from another carriage house up on the hill. It did not take my cousin Arthur long to figure out the connection. He called a council, assigned each of us a post, and that night the plan went into operation. He climbed the tree after dark and installed a pulley hook in the trunk while we installed another one in a window frame in the upper floor of the carriage house. Then we took a rope and with muffled orders, groans, and many false starts, we finally managed a shuttle system in the form of a berry basket between the tree and the shed. Just what our thinking was, in going to such elaborate lengths to get something we could have had just by surreptitiously climbing the tree, escapes me at the moment.

Anyhow, the next day after school, we acted as sentries in strategic places, gave Art the signal that it was safe to climb the tree, and scrambled up to our end of the shuttle in the carriage house. It was simple. He filled the basket—we pulled it in. It worked like a charm for awhile—until the day my aunt glanced out her kitchen window and saw a basket of apples floating mysteriously through the air. Justice was quick and fierce. We smarted for hours.

Saturday was always a big day. We all drove into town in Henry. In the morning the groceries and haircuts and errands were taken care of, and at noon we went to lunch in the swankiest restaurant in town. There were white tablecloths, an orchestra, white-coated waiters, and fabulous colored lights playing everywhere from a revolving chandelier. Eating there was partly for fun and partly academic. We were taken there to be instructed. We had to read the menu, order for ourselves, sit quietly, speak softly, butter only a portion of our roll at a time, use the proper utensils, say please and thank you—and behave with impeccable decorum while we discussed in grown-up fashion the topics of the day. It was a sort of field work for the theory in manners and deportment we got at home. Mother was, rich or poor, a Comstock too.

As wonderful as that treat was, it was not the real highlight of the week. That came early Saturday morning and you had to wait for a Saturday when it was your turn. When your turn came, mother would lean quietly over your bed and whisper your name. You would leap up and get dressed hurriedly, and in quiet conspiracy the two of you would sneak out, fishing poles over your shoulders, a can of worms (dug behind the barn the day before) between you, and make for the barbed-wire fence that skirted the meadow. You would help each other crawl through, and follow the path to the pond. Then, hooks baited and corks bobbing on the ripples, you would sit and talk softly and lazily, soaking in the dawn and the dew and the loveliness of God's awakening world. The placid mirror of water reflected the surrounding daisies in rippling duplicate, and as you watched, you could talk to mother in private, have her all to yourself, chuckle with her, bare your heart to her, and drink in her understanding and her wisdom. And the wonder and the beauty of it would sink to the very depths of your soul and heal every wound and clear up every puzzle that had accumulated since you'd been there last. You would be back at breakfast time, proudly showing your catch to the now-awake family, and then the fish were cleaned and fried for breakfast. But catching the fish was only incidental. The real joy was having her all to yourself. I did not realize until I was grown that those were "private interviews"—the only way she could get to know each of us as individuals and let us know her.

In spite of the fact that she had been up at dawn and carted us through a hectic day, we were shampooed on Saturday night, and off to Sunday school and church on Sunday morning, scrubbed and pressed till we shone. We sat in the pew with gramma. Mother sang in the choir. How she could manage to stand, much less sing, I'll never know. But sing she did, and still managed to drive us somewhere Sunday afternoon, march us off to Christian Endeavor Sunday evening, and have enough energy to make popcorn balls Sunday night.

She had a sweet alto voice, and an amazing ability to pick out any tune on the piano and play it by ear. She could play "MacNamara's Band"—and hymns—and everything in between. She could never pass the piano without playing it, even if there was time for only one chorus. To her, hymn singing was prayer and praise—and worship. She would play and sing softly to herself when she was in trouble, and fill the house with joyful hymns when she was happy. She could never read a note, but was determined that we would. So we all went through an agonizing period of piano lessons and filled the air with a cacophony of scales and discords. Mother was slow to admit defeat, but in the end it was a dismal failure.

Mother spoke two languages. And like most linguists, she could think better in her own. For the most part she spoke ours, but in moments of absent-mindedness or stress she would lapse into the other one, which threw the family into a furor of confusion because we could never quite get the hang of it. The thing that made it difficult was that the same word never meant the same thing twice. The various nuances of ordinary languages are confusing at first, it is true. But once you learn them you can depend upon them. They never change. In mother's other language, however, words like thingamabob, whatchamacallit, thingamajig, thingamacallit, whatchamajig, jigger, do-dad, dydo, whatsit, whosit, etc., could mean anything at all. They were all interchangeable and never twice the same.

We had various methods of expediting the translation. If things were fairly quiet we could bridge the language barrier by applying the rules of the game in which you guessed the object your opponent was thinking of by walking in various directions while he told you whether you were cold, warm or hot. Cold meant you were way off the beam —warm meant you were getting closer—and hot meant the object was at hand. So when she would say, "Will you be a lamb and get the whatsit?" we would say, "Where?"

"You know where. It's in the top right drawer of the whosit along with the rest of them." And she would gesticulate vaguely toward the end of the room where there was a huge cabinet and a desk—and both of them had lots of drawers.

"Here?" we would say, moving toward the desk.

"No—the dydo."

"Here?" The cabinet was the only possibility left.

"Yes. Some black whatchamacallit, number sixty."

Well that could only mean black thread.

But in times of emergency she could throw us into a panic.

"Quick—the thingamabob!"

"The *what?*"

"The whatchamacallit. And *please* hurry!"

In a case like this we would resort to the game of twenty questions and by elimination and clues, track it down with great efficiency.

"Is it in the living room?"

"No—in the whatchamajig!"

"The kitchen?"

"Yes—and *hurry!*"

"Do you want us to get it or do something with it?"

"Turn the jigger off under it before it burns!"

Oh. There we had it. We scrambled to turn the gas off under the lamb stew.

The thing that saved us was the fact that she had no other language of her own for verbs. If we could pin her down to a verb, we had it made. I've always been grateful for this. If we had ever had to conjugate her verbs I doubt if we'd have survived.

Fortunately you can learn anything if you keep at it long enough, by instinct if no other way. The other night I phoned her and, three thousand miles apart, we conversed freely with no trouble at all.

"How's your thingamabob coming along?"

"Oh fine. I have five whatsits written. But I'm having a little trouble with the whatchamacallits."

"I'm sorry about that, sweetheart. Don't get discouraged."

"Oh I'm not discouraged. Once I get the dydos all straightened out the rest goes easily."

"Well I'm glad. Let me know if Mr. Whosits at the publishing house likes it."

"I'll do that, mother. I'll let you know what he thinks."

Which shows the repercussions of years of proximity.

It was during my high school years that mother became an unreasonable fiend who didn't know anything and didn't understand anything and of everything she didn't understand the most was me. She didn't understand that I *liked* my room in chaos. Or that I wasn't lazy, I was just meditating. Or that I wasn't nasty, I was just misunderstood. And she was horrid when I cut up four good dresses and dyed them black to cut up and make one black dress, a perfectly reasonable thing to do. And then she committed the epitome of all crimes—got married and went off on a honeymoon at the tottering old age of thirty-eight!

I graduated from high school and went off to further my schooling in a rage, with intent to disown my family.

The fact that I did not feel close to her during those years has done more than anything else to keep my head above water during the years my sons did not feel close to me. There is a great gulf and you cannot bridge it. The child becomes an adult and the process is such a raging turmoil that it is only by the grace of God that we survive it at all. But the vagaries of my adolescence are beside the point here. Mother had emerged from her self-enforced loneliness and was happily married, and I did not have the sense to appreciate it.

Her happiness was short-lived. Glaucoma, discovered too late, sent her into surgery with little hope that she would see again. I went back home for summer vacation, numb with terror and repentance. We waited for weeks after surgery for the glasses that would tell us the outcome. The day they arrived, she went into her bedroom alone and knelt and prayed before she opened the package. Then we heard her fumble with the wrappings—and then we heard her say: "Oh, God. I cannot see." It was the only time I'd ever heard her really cry. But the next morning she woke us all up with a start. She was playing the piano and singing "Sweeter As the Years Go By."

In the years that followed there were several more operations with only light-and-shadow vision restored. And then my dear stepfather died.

My aunt, whose farm we'd lived on, was alone now too, so they lived together in mother's house. And mother kept things humming.

She found new ways of doing things with the agility of a cat in the dark, absolutely refused all our attempts to baby her, joined everything the Blind Society had to offer, rolled bandages and made dressings for the Red Cross, sealed envelopes, made Christmas wreaths—and went to visit blind people who were despondent! And people beat a path to her door to visit, to have a cup of tea, to sing some hymns—and to hear her ringing laugh. She had more friends now than ever before. And her life was full.

The day I decided to write the script in this chapter was the day I barged in on her for a chat, and she was busy at the dining room table, poring over a huge book. She announced cheerfully that it was Braille and she had a teacher and was determined to learn to read all over again. She knew, she said, she was too old to learn it, so she'd asked God to help her.

That day I discovered mother all over again in a different way. She had always been "mother." I had never really seen her before as a woman. I thought about it on the way home. And what I thought, I jotted down. It turned out to be my

Mother's Day radio program a few weeks later.

* * * * *

DEAR MOTHER

Dear Mother,

It tells us in Proverbs—"Who can find a virtuous woman? For her price is far above rubies. . . . She openeth her mouth with wisdom; and in her tongue is the law of kindness. Her children arise up, and call her blessed. . . ."

I've often wondered just when a human being first becomes aware of his mother—I know that, subconsciously, a baby is first aware of his mother when he drinks of the sweetness of her breast and satisfies not only a physical hunger but a deeper hunger and need for love. But when does he become aware of her as another human being with desires and fears and hopes and deep, deep disappointments?

When did I first become aware of you as a *person?* When we were very small—and you sat up far into the night for weeks before Christmas while everything the most exacting dolly needs in clothing and bedclothing materialized like magic under your clever fingers — and when Christmas came, and the living room was transformed into a veritable fairyland of lights and sparkle and happiness—I wasn't aware of you then. I didn't know you slipped away to stand in the closet where his clothes were hung, to cry with loneliness because he was dead — I didn't know with the knowledge that aches that there was a Flanders Field and my father was buried there, and your heart was broken. I just knew it was Christmas and you had provided me with my heart's desire because it was the sole aim and purpose and reason for your being—to please and delight me.

And through the years when you worked all day while gramma cared for us — and came home at night and did the work she could not do—I wasn't aware of you, or of her either — oh, how I could love her now!

What a miscellaneous collection of driftwood our family was! Orphans, and refugees from broken homes, banded together in one family—each one a problem for psychoanalysis, I suppose, if we'd ever heard of it then. With such a collection of assorted temperaments and backgrounds, it's a wonder we didn't all blow up and disappear right out of sight!

I used to wonder how you ever put up with the rest of them—I used to wonder how you could put up with Arthur — with his red hair and incorrigible teasing—did you know I used to lie awake and imagine dramatic court scenes where I was being tried for having hit him on the head with a hammer and killed him—and of course the judge, after hearing what an *outrageous* boy he was, commended me highly and gave me a reward. It was an outlet, I suppose, certainly better than killing him—which I'm awfully glad I did not do—for he's now the father of two wonderful sons and the head of a prosperous business.

I used to wonder how you could put up— but why go on? I guess all my childhood I thought that life would be wonderful if you would only get rid of the rest of them and have more time for just me. You poor darling—you never once had time for yourself — how selfish I was.

How did you do it? How did you work all week—and have the courage to scrub us all to a standstill and march us off to church each Sunday? How did you have the energy to sing in the choir? Even as I write this letter, you amaze me all over again.

You must have taught me a great deal more than I realized. Remember the poetry

I wrote? "No artist can paint the color . . . of the beautiful morning sky . . . the yellow that splashes on treetops . . . at noon when the sun is high. . . . No artist can match the colors . . . in a lovely setting sun . . . ta da *da* da da *da* da da *da* da . . . (forgotten that part) . . . da da *da* when the day is done. If I could but express myself . . . that feeling that's inside . . . Man cannot do anything . . . lest he in God abide." I was eight years old when I scribbled that on a paper napkin. I must have absorbed it from you. My whole concept of God, I absorbed from you.

Through those years I was aware of you as a mother—I remember loving you dearly, striving to please you, glorying in the times we had together alone, when we went fishing together and talked softly in the quiet early morning, and my soul was flooded with the happiness of having you all to myself.

And then there were the years when I wasn't aware of you at all. I was too painfully aware of myself. I was growing in every direction and not like the lovely lady I'd always been in my daydreams — but fat and ugly and stupid with my nose shiny and my feet too big! Were you there? Were you there at all? I didn't see you. The emotional upheaval of my metamorphosis was too terrific. I couldn't grow up gently, as a flower—I exploded, like a cork out of a bottle. How could you stand me? How could you encourage me to speak, to write, how could you see any possibilities in me when I was such a muttonhead?

Do you remember when there was a celebration for the cast in a school play and I planned for weeks to go, and pressed my dress at least eight times the day before—and do you remember the mounting panic as my face broke out with amazing speed—and the depths of my despair when, the last minute, I was forced to face the fact that I had chicken pox? You were the only one who understood my humiliation.

But for the most part, I wasn't aware of you at all. You didn't see anything the way I did. You didn't know anything either. You wanted me to get enough sleep and eat vegetables and think babies were *cute*. Those years must have been tough on you.

Then you emerged from your self-enforced loneliness and married Dad and I was horrified. I couldn't imagine how two people so *old* could possibly fall in love! (You were only thirty-eight.) And I went away to school.

How awful to think that when you faced the blackest part of your life, I was aware of you the least. While I was busy getting my education and trying my wings, you were fighting a losing battle to keep your eyesight.

After the first operation on your dear eyes, wonderful improvement, joyous hope, and then the relentless infection began to destroy again. Through the operations that followed, the same hope, the same marvelous improvement at first—the same bitter disappointment. And through it all, though we protested, you insisted on "Business as usual"—and never once did you even think of not doing your own work. Like an ingenious blood-vessel that has been truncated in one direction, you promptly found another way to do it!

I remember, after one operation, when weeks went by for healing, and then the glasses came — the glasses that would tell whether this one was a success. You went alone to your room and knelt and asked God to give you the grace and the strength to bear it, if you could not see. Who of us can understand the anguish that was yours as you fumbled at the wrappings and found the glasses and put them on—

"Oh, God—God. I cannot see—I cannot see. . . ."

Then Dad died, and there was still another operation after that and we watched you so closely, because we said, "If this one isn't successful, it will finish her—she will not be able to bear it."

The flashes of light came—and then stopped—and left you once more to a world of shadows and near blackness. But we had underestimated the depth of your character. Because, not long ago, you announced to me matter-of-factly that you were learning Braille. "I was going to take a few piano lessons if I had my sight again," you said. "But I decided to learn Braille instead. I'll be able to read my Bible. See? I'm on the B's. I just read 'Big Bill's baby is bald.' It surprised me so I had to laugh when I got to 'bald.'"

I didn't know what to say. I still don't. I stand in awe before your quiet, uncomplaining strength.

For at last I *am* aware of you, not as a child is, but as one woman who is aware of another. I didn't understand you then because I did not have the capacity to understand.

There is strength in the warp and woof of the tapestry of your life, and woven through all is a golden thread of joyous laughter and song that was always a part of you — and then there is another thread, a scarlet thread, for though the price of a virtuous woman is indeed "far above rubies" — you have not thought your own righteousness would ever get you into heaven — but have humbly claimed the righteousness of our Lord Jesus Christ.

I'm proud of you. I'm proud of you — and I thank God for you. May He bless you and keep you on this Mother's Day — and in the days to come, until you see Him . . . face to face. Always,

Your little girl
Ethel

* * * * *

Yes, my mother was a great woman. I did not want to say this right off. I wanted it to sneak up on you the way it has sneaked up on me, through the years. Because her greatness isn't the kind that makes headlines and gets in "Who's Who" and stays aloof, leaving us discouraged and thinking, "I could never do *that*." It is the kind that is right down to earth with the rest of us. She was great because she was "faithful in little things," which is something we can all attain, and which is of great worth to God.

In Micah we are asked, "What doth the Lord require of thee, but to do justly, and to love mercy, and to walk humbly with thy God?" (6:8).

She taught us — "And thou shalt teach them (God's commandments) diligently unto thy children . . . " (Deut. 6:7).

She trained us — "Train up a child in the way he should go . . ." (Prov. 22:6).

She punished us — "Chasten thy son while there is hope . . . " (Prov. 19:18).

She loved us — " . . . but the greatest of these is love" (I Cor. 13:13).

She always remembered the good — "Whatsoever things are true, whatsoever things are honest, whatsoever things are just, whatsoever things are pure, whatsoever things are lovely, whatsoever things are of good report; if there be any virtue, and if there be any praise, think on these things" (Phil. 4:8).

She would not give up—"Let us not be weary in well doing . . ." (Gal. 6:9).

And she was a happy woman. I mentioned at the beginning that she never seemed to get ahold of the fact that from a human standpoint she had little to be happy about and went right on being happy anyway. The reason is not so strange. The reason is that her happiness did not depend on happenings. She had a built-in joy and that joy was the presence of God. It had nothing to do with her circumstances; it was always there whether they were good or bad. She was so completely in God's hands that no matter how things looked, she had everything to be happy about. Was not God still in heaven? And did He not know? And did He not care?

She had the sense of constant discovery children

have — and too many adults lose too soon — that made all of life an adventure, even the simplest things. Perhaps her secret was that she never thought of personal happiness as a goal or as an end in itself. It was a sort of by-product that was popping up at every corner while she was busy doing other things.

But to get from the past to the present and bring us up to date: My mother *is* a happy woman. I phoned her tonight from my hotel room in San Francisco and told her I had just written this chapter. She protested violently — what on earth could I *think* of about her to fill a whole chapter? And then we got talking about Henry — and I heard her ringing laughter over thousands of miles . . .

CHAPTER 2

MASKS

Lift not the festal mask! — enough to know,
No scene of mortal life but teems with mortal woe.
Sir Walter Scott, *Lord of the Isles.*

One of Nathaniel Hawthorne's most thought-provoking stories is "The Minister's Black Veil," and one of his most enigmatic characters is the man who wore it. He was a young minister in a small parish who astonished his congregation one Sunday morning by appearing with a black crepe veil over his face. He kept it on while he read the Scriptures and while he prayed and they went from astonishment to a vague uneasiness. But when he kept it on through his sermon on secret sin, they went into a mild state of shock. The real shock came later, though, as the days went on and then the weeks and he did not take the veil off. The townspeople speculated, some in awe, some in fear — what dreadful secret lay behind that black crepe veil?

Well, the years went on and he never did remove it. And the story concerns the effect that veil had both on his life and the lives around him. It completely isolated him from his fellow men. At the end Hawthorne said: "All through life that piece of crepe had hung between him and the world; it had separated him from cheerful brotherhood and woman's love, and kept him in that saddest of all prisons, his own heart."

But the real shocker comes when on his deathbed he cries out to the spectators gathered around: "Why do you tremble at me? It is not my black veil that has kept people from me — it is what it stands for. For no one shows his inmost heart — to his friend or to his lover — we even vainly try to shrink from God. I look around me and lo — on EVERY face — a black veil!"

Well!

The tale leaves one with the eerie feeling that everybody who crosses one's path — and indeed, one's closest friends and even loved ones — are wearing "black veils," or masks, and one can never really get to *know* anybody. "We pass [other human beings] like ships in the night" and "each of us is an isle of loneliness" are desolate thoughts indeed. But in the last cold analysis, they are true.

Edna St. Vincent Millay's "we sit in each other's souls" is a beautiful concept of friendship, but the truth of the matter is that the most we can ever do is sit in the vestibules. Even those of us who are most communicative and uninhibited in airing our secret thoughts to those nearest us, can never really do a thorough job, for there are too many doors that lead to dark unexplored corridors and the doors are locked and we ourselves do not know what is behind them.

I had a friend once who used to lament periodically, "I have quite given up hope that anybody will ever understand me!" She was remarkably intelligent in every other way, so her naiveté in this area was surprising. For naturally nobody really understood her and nobody ever would.

Sometimes there are doors we are afraid to open.

Another friend once asked me to find out the whole truth about a problem she was enmeshed in, for I had access to facts that she did not. I was foolish enough to tell her part of the truth, but she could not believe even that and I thereby lost a friend. I did not realize that she could not face opening that door, but I could never hold it against her, for there are doors in my life I've been afraid to open, too.

Masks can hide so many things that it would be impossible to tackle the subject in one chapter, or even in one book. But they fall into two general categories. The sorrows and wounds that are tangible — we can describe them. We know when they happened and how. And the intangibles — the vast and deep morass in each of us that can never in this life be dredged. I shall never try in this chapter, nor indeed would I ever try, to discourse at any length upon this second category. In the first place I would be beyond my depth. In the second place I have no intention of peeking behind masks and dissecting my friends and loved ones, and even less intention of peeking behind my own to dissect myself.

It is enough for us to understand that everybody lives behind one — the people who are hard to get to know, the ones who are difficult to get along with, the ones we envy because they seem to have been blessed with all material blessings and a problem-free life — and even the artless carefree ones who are always gay, always good for a laugh.

For the story in this chapter, I have chosen a radio script about two women. One had a serious problem, and she had wandered in the Door of Hope Mission for wayward girls, in New York City. When she found she was to be interviewed by, of all people, Mrs. Whittemore herself, she cried out to the attendant — well she cried out many things, but the essence of them was: "How can *she* understand?"

Indeed it did seem unlikely. Mrs. Whittemore was a wealthy society woman who might have founded the Door of Hope Mission as a hobby and taken a dilettante interest in such things just to show what a good fellow she was. But as the story unfolds, Mrs. Whittemore's mask is tilted a bit, and we find she is quite human after all. I chose this story because one of our greatest failings in this direction is to look at other persons who were born in the proper families, made the proper marriages, bore the proper children and lived happily ever after — and think in our hearts: "How could they understand sorrow?" And we quite forget that they are wearing masks too.

You will meet Frankie in this story too — and at the risk of being discursive I want to explain something about him, because he seems too good to be true. He *was* true, nonetheless; I have not doctored him up to prove a point. In all the conversation between Frankie and his mother, including the tender name he dubbed her, I have lifted their words verbatim out of biography. There was no poetic license need for dramatic effect; indeed, in all my life I could never dream up words as beautiful as Frankie's, nor would I dare attempt to put such insight into the heart of a child if it were fiction. It would be a travesty on realism — too much to expect anyone to swallow.

So true it is, the whole of it, except for Jeannie and the matron at the Door of Hope, who are products of my imagination. But I suspect there were hundreds of Jeannies who passed through the portals of the Door of Hope.

* * * * *

LITTLE MATE

There's a certain pseudo glamour about being in the public eye — even in Christian service. There shouldn't be, of course, but there sometimes is. . . . It struck me all over again, that morning, while I was helping Jeannie on with clean clothes. Jeannie was a new girl, just come to us at the Door of Hope Mission, and she was a little bit resentful. I was used to that, tho'. I'd been a matron there for years. And I'd seen them come and go. They were often resentful when they came. Or seemed to be. They were really scared.

"I'm afraid of her," she said. "What's she like?"

"Who? Mother Whittemore?" I said. "Well she's certainly no one to be afraid of! Here's your watch. She's a great Christian."

She took the watch. "It ought to be easy for a woman like that to be a great Christian."

"Well." I cleared my throat and took my time. I knew what I was going to say. And I took my time getting around to it. "She's a friend — and adviser — to hundreds of girls who pass through these doors. I suppose it's hard to conceive that she has a private life."

"Private life? Huh! She's got some private life! She's got everything. Riches, position, beautiful home, a husband who loves her. Why couldn't a woman with such a life be a great Christian?"

"It would seem easy, wouldn't it?" I said reasonably. "One long procession of trips and lectures and noble deeds. Surely that's a life to envy. But there's another side to Mother Whittemore. First, she had to get down on her knees and ask the Lord to save her, same as you or I."

"Yeah?"

"And second — she's every inch a wife — and mother — and woman."

"She's got kids, huh?" Ah. I had her.

"Oh yes." I said. "Several children. Wonderful family and a story could be told about each one — but I was thinking of Frankie."

"Frankie?"

"Your watch reminded me of him. The story of Frankie just gets all mixed up in your thinking with a watch, somehow. Want to hear it?"

"What've I got to lose?" she shrugged.

Well she was a captive audience. And I had nothing to lose either. "That's right. We've got a good thirty minutes to wait. Might as well have some coffee. Want some?"

I didn't wait for her answer. I poured it from the pot on the sideboard and sat down and made myself comfortable, as if there was nothing else to do anyhow — we might as well talk. She pulled her clean wrapper around her and sat down. She was heavy and miserable with unwanted pregnancy, but a little less on guard.

"There we are," I said, as if we had been doing this for years. And I cleared my throat and began.

"Before I was a matron here, I worked in the Whittemore home. And Frankie — well, there was just something special about Frankie. He was so friendly and full of love and laughter — he had friends from the most important dignitaries in his mother and father's circles — down to us in the servants' quarters. We called him 'Little Mate.' His real name was Frankie Whittemore, but we seldom thought of it, for his grandpa had called him 'Little Mate' and he'd called his grandpa 'Captain.' Before his grandpa died, they'd gone off on many an adventure together — and afterward, the name had always stuck. He was a funny little fellow, Frankie . . . used to come around to the kitchen often. . . .

'Hi! Good morning!' he'd say.

'Good morning,' I'd say.

'May I come in?'

'Noooo. You certainly can't. I just scrubbed the floor and it isn't dry yet.'

'Oh. How long do I have to wait?'

'What do you want?'

'You know — a cookie.'

'I thought so! You have to wait till it's dry — that's how long you have to wait.'

'Oh.'

'Why don't you go play and come back later?'

'Say, I've got a death-defying idea.'

'What's that?'

'If I could put the ladder from the counter to the sink, and crawl in through the window, and jump from the window to the ladder, to the sink to the cupboard, I wouldn't have to wait till the floor gets dry.'

'Go 'way with you! You'll do no such thing.

Find something to do. Go play with your ball.'

'I can't. It's up on the roof.'

'How'd it get up there?'

'I threw it up after my hat to get my hat down.'

'How'd *that* get — never mind — don't tell me. I can guess.'

"He'd laughed. 'That's right. I threw that up too. I didn't think it would really land. When I get that cookie, may I have two? One for Tommy? He never gets cookies?'

'Goodness yes. You're always thinking of somebody else. Now go way with you or I'll sweep you right off the porch!'

'You wouldn't dare! I'm your friend!'

"That's the way it usually went — Frankie was always thinking of someone else. And into everything! When he wasn't helping some other kid out of a jam he was jumping off docks and nearly drowning. And when he wasn't busy drowning he was sliding off roofs and nearly breaking his neck. But about the watch. I guess wanting a watch was in his mind a long time before he actually got it. He probably told his mother about it — he told her everything. They were very close. And they had the most grown-up conversations.

'Mother—'

'Hello, darling—'

'Mrs. Whittemore, I believe?'

'Yes, I am Mrs. Whittemore.'

'Are you *the* Mrs. Whittemore?'

'The very same. And who might you be, young man?'

'Well, I'm Frankie Whittemore, your son. Better known as Little Mate. Remember me?"

'Why *of course*. Now I recognize you. How do you *do*.'

"And they would talk, or fall silent, as the mood struck them. Sometimes they would go into gales of laughter. And sometimes they'd be very serious. Frankie had a quick and sensitive mind. And she would steer his thoughts and then listen while he explored them. She was good at listening. But one day they got into a conversation that — well neither of them knew at the time how significant it was. It was about the watch. It began in the usual way.

'How do you *do*,' he said. And then, 'Move over.'

'Funny face. What do you want?'

'Want? Nothing! Just to be with you, Pet.'

"And then he sighed and leaned against her. "I'm tired,' he said.

'You? Tired?'

'My bones ache.'

'Your *bones*? We'll have to have the doctor look at you.' And, after a pause. 'Love mamma, darling?'

'Love you? Hm! Well I guess! Do you know what I'd like to have — if I could have anything I wanted?'

'What?'

'A watch.'

'You're too young for a watch.'

'I know. But I'd like to have one, all the same. I'd wind it and know what time it was.'

'What do you care about time?'

'Whether time is long or short — you know. Anyhow I'd like to have a watch.'

"It was strange that he'd be so crazy for a watch — and think so much about time, 'cause time figured so importantly in his life, it turned out.

"It wasn't long after that, that aching bones and tired spells added up to a real serious thing, and we realized how sick he was. From then on, Mother Whittemore's private heartbreak got pretty mixed up with her public self. . . .

"It started with a routine checkup and then more doctors and then they ordered Frankie to bed. We were upset but we still didn't realize, or we didn't want to. I guess we didn't want to.

"The day the blow fell, I'll never forget. She was in the upstairs hall talking with the doctor and I was putting away linen and heard it all.

'Mrs. Whittemore—' the doctor said.

'Yes, Doctor?'

'Your son's condition is far more serious than we thought at first. Now with great care, we can—'

'What are you trying to tell me, Doctor? That my son is going to be ill all his life?'

"He paused a moment. 'That your son isn't going to live, Mrs. Whittemore.'

'Oh!' I couldn't see her face. But I could hear it all in her voice. Anguish. And a desperate hope. 'How long, doctor?'

'A few weeks — months, perhaps.'

"I dropped some towels and scurried to pick them up and waited for her to answer. It turned out she didn't have to. Somebody called up from downstairs.

'Mrs. Whittemore — the committee's downstairs in the drawing-room — about the extension on the Door of Hope.'

'Yes', she called back. 'I'll be down in a few moments. Tell them — ask them to wait. I'm going in to see Frankie.' She left us there and went into his room.

'Hi, Little Mate,' she said.

'Hi, Pet.'

'My what a lot of pillows. You're sure propped up.'

'Um hm. Aye aye, Pet. Can breathe better this way.'

'Little Mate—'

'Aye, aye, Pet. What?'

'Nothing.'

'Would you please hand me that vase?'

'Um hm. What's that?'

'I've been saving. A dollar and seventy cents.'

'My, that's a fortune.'

'Is that enough — to send a boy to camp?'

'Oh my darling,' she said. Then quickly, 'Look —we'll—papa and I will send a boy to camp. Why don't you put that toward a watch?'

'A *watch*? Ohhh.' He struggled with the decision. 'But I was going to send a boy to camp. I shouldn't change my mind.'

'You send a boy to camp with your money, then. And papa and I will buy you a watch— just for fun. I'll buy you one next time I go shopping.'

'Oh *boy!* A watch! I wanted a watch more than anything!'

"And so it was decided...

"My, the day that watch was bought! It was the most important day in Frankie's life. He waited with his nurse, his little face feverish, his eyes bright.

'Nurse—'

'Yes, dear?'

'How long has she been gone?'

'Most two hours now. You must be patient.'

'What time is it?'

41

'Four o'clock.'

'I wish I'd asked her to buy a chain too. It would be so nice to have a watch with a chain —he raised himself beyond his strength. 'I hear someone coming up the stairs! Maybe it's — Ohhhhhhhhh.'

"She came in then, triumphant.

'Hello, Little Mate!'

'Aye, aye, Pet!'

'Here!' She sat on the edge of his bed and opened the package. 'Here it is. There.'

'Ohhhhh. And a chain! A watch and a chain! Isn't it a beauty!'

'It's all wound and set.'

'Same as yours?'

'Same as mine.'

'It's a beauty.' He fondled it lovingly.

'Love me, darling?' She said it playfully. It was a part of a routine.

'Love you? Hm! Well I guess!'

"The days went by quickly, too quickly. And they were all mixed up with time.

'You've been with me all day, Pet.'

'I love being with you.'

'Don't forget to wind my watch.'

'I won't.'

'Same as yours?'

'Same as mine.'

'Then I'll know what time it is when I wake up in the night.'

"Time. Emma Whittemore carried on her work at the Door of Hope Mission by remote control and spent day and night with her son. And that little watch ticked away precious time, numbering the hours of Frankie's life. Not a minute could be wasted—not a minute wasted to prepare that little mate to meet his 'captain' grandpa — and the Captain of his salvation—the Lord Jesus Christ.

"There were drives in the country, Frankie propped up on pillows, leaning on her shoulder —and hours poring over books and playing simple games—and hours over God's Word. During those days there were two Emma Whittemores. One, the capable superintendent of the Girls' Home, solver of other people's problems. The other, Emma Whittemore, all mother—all woman. And on that last day—

"It happened while she was giving her secretary the routine orders.

'Tell the committee to report to me on Monday. You'd better drop a note to the folks in Boston—tell them I won't be there. Postpone it indefinitely. And while you're at it—'

'Mrs. Whittemore—' a nurse called from upstairs.

'Yes?'

'You'd better come. It's Frankie.'

"She flew up the stairs. But when she went into his room she was quiet and serene.

43

'Hi, Little Mate.'

'Hi, Pet.'

'Oh, my darling. Can I change your position?'

'No. I feel good now. Pain is gone. I — just had some things to tell you.'

'Uh huh.'

'Louie can have all of my presents. Give baby some of my toys.'

'Yes—'

'Give Hennie my knife. Emma my seal ring. Minnie my pocketbook.'

'Why, Little Mate—'

'Mama'—his eyes demanded the truth. 'I'm going to die, aren't I?'

"She struggled with her voice. 'Would—would you be afraid to go with Jesus?'

'No, mamma.'

'Then—yes. You are going, darling. With Jesus.'

"He looked at her. And the wisdom of the ages was in his eyes. 'Was that hard for you to say?'

'Very hard.'

'Don't cry, Pet. Ask me if I love you.'

'Do you love me?'

'Love you? Hm! Well, I guess. Give Papa all my money. He's so good. There's 'most four dollars saved. And I want you to have my watch. Only sell it and give the money to the Door of Hope.'

"It was too much. She looked at him, wordless, her throat aching, her eyes stark and naked. At the end, she was the helpless one, he the comforter. But then he was closer to God. He was already away. He raised himself as he had not been able to do for weeks. His eyes were brilliant.

'Aw, Pet,' he cried. 'Don't cry. I'll give your love to Grandpa and wait till you come.' And then—and it was a cry of triumph, 'Get on—get on the other side of the cross.'

'What do you mean?' She whispered it. They were on holy ground.

'The *other* side!' He cried. And then, 'Why, Mama, I'm going to be all well!'

"And he sank back and the watch slipped from his hands and he was gone.

"We found her there holding the watch, her head on his breast. And in her eyes was a look of wonder.

"The other side of the cross!

"This side — sorrow, crucifixion. The other side — resurrection, victory . . .

"Next day a telegram came from Frankie's grandmother, saying: 'PUT LITTLE MATE ON THE RIGHT SIDE OF HIS CAPTAIN.' Little Mate had gone to meet the other Captain too — the Captain of his salvation — the Lord Jesus Christ."

Jeannie and I were silent for some time after

45

I finished my story. We'd long since finished our coffee. The spell was still upon us. I didn't say any more. I didn't preach. I'd wait for the story to settle, like the coffee grounds.

"I'm awful glad you told me that," she said at last. "What a kid. And it makes *her* more human. More real."

"Jeannie," I said. "Whenever you see a great Christian whose life is serene and joyful and powerful — it doesn't always mean there haven't been wounds. Look deep for sorrow in everyone's life — it is always there. Sometimes it's the sorrow that made that Christian great. Sometimes — Oh! Here she is now." The sliding doors opened. "Good morning Mrs. Whittemore," I said.

"Good morning," she said, looking at Jeannie.

"This is Jeannie," I said. "Just come this morning."

"Good morning, Jeannie." Emma Whittemore's face was frank and down-to-earth and without any pretense of piety or sticky kindness; Jeannie would not have understood either. Then, "Won't you come into the parlor and tell me about it?"

They eyed each other for a moment, two women. Then they went into the parlor and the doors slid closed behind them.

* * * * *

Well.

Mother Whittemore's mask hid a tangible wound. The story is true, all true. But as we said before, masks don't always hide great sorrow. Some of the most trouble-free persons we know are trapped behind their masks in the insoluble complexities of their own natures.

My favorite aunt was one who wore her mask with uncommunicative dignity. I lived on her farm as a child, knew her up until her death, often heard her laugh, but never really knew what made her tick. Her mask never slipped in front of others. The only time I ever remember that it did was one day when a couple of errant bossies (cows were always "bossies" to her) wandered up by the main house and got into her tiny flower bed and trampled it to bits. She got them back quietly, speaking to them in gentle tones. Then she called a farmhand to mend the fence where they'd escaped, and went back to her devastated flower bed and knelt, digging her fists into the ground, and wept silently. The weeping done, she simply went on about her duties and the subject was not mentioned again. The mask was back on.

It is true that the exacting business of helping to make the farm pay took all her time and she never had a moment for herself. To indulge in a flower garden was heresy! It is true that wherever they lived, the most she had time for was one tiny spot of beauty—her little flower bed. And it is true that

47

the flowers were her greatest joy—her one indulgence. But I do not think the trampled flower bed, in itself, was what made her cry. Perhaps it was symbolic of all the beauty in her life. It is possible that years of frustration and a great accumulation of pent-up disappointments went into that weeping. We never knew for sure. She was not one to air her private dreams. She died in quiet uncomplaining dignity, and her mask went with her.

God makes it very explicit that we are all behind masks and, what is more, they are, beyond a certain point, impenetrable. And He has four important things to say about it.

First, we cannot thoroughly understand others. For "man looketh on the outward appearance, but the Lord looketh on the heart" (I Sam. 16:7).

Second, we cannot really understand ourselves. "Man's goings are of the Lord; how can a man then understand his own way?" (Prov. 20:24).

And third, we cannot judge others, and He tells us in no uncertain terms that we had better not try. "There is one lawgiver, who is able to save and to destroy: who art thou that judgest another?" (James 4:12).

And last, we are not even to judge ourselves. Paul thunders: "But with me it is a very small thing that I should be judged of you, or of man's judgment: "yea, *I judge not mine own self. For I know nothing by myself* . . . but he that judgeth me is the Lord" (I Cor. 4:3,4).

Of course we are to confess our sins—but the distinction here is that we are not to take it upon ourselves to decide what our own motives are in anything we do—good *or* bad. Only God knows what is behind our masks. The ways in which we can deceive ourselves are so many and so subtle and so *reasonable* that we are helpless without the Holy Spirit's searching. The real motivation behind some of our behavior, if faced, would give us quite a jolt.

"I fell into this sin because that person tempted me. If he hadn't crossed my path nothing like that would ever have happened." (That person ran into an incipient desire in you that was clamoring for attention all the time, and although your physical feet did drag a bit, didn't the feet of your mind "run swiftly to destruction?" *But every man is tempted, when he is drawn away of his own lust, and enticed.*)

"I am always giving because I am so generous." (You are not. Giving gives you a sense of power. With you it is a fetish and the recipients of your favors are forevermore tied to you in constant demands for gratitude and reminders of your love. Your gifts do not have strings—they have nooses.)

"I fell into the habit of drinking through despondency after my children got married and left home. I had devoted my life to them and they were all I had to live for—and I still worry so about them." (Or were you so emotionally dependent upon your children and had you so enslaved them with devotion and demands for gratitude that they were glad to get out from under it, and now you don't have the courage to live without substituting another prop?)

"I slaved for an alcoholic husband, just threw away the best years of my life—and now that he is gone, *of course* I'm bitter over the years I lost." (Come now. Didn't you have a sneaking feeling of superiority and power over another human being, and didn't you enjoy being a martyr—and when he died and you no longer had anything to complain of and no reason to exact sympathy from your friends—didn't it knock the props from under you and isn't that the real reason why you went off and had that nervous breakdown?)

"I used to like him, but now we live in different worlds. He has *changed* so!" (Has he really? Or is it you who have changed? Can it be that you could easily like him as an inferior, but you cannot accept him as a success?)

"I felt it was best for the group if she dropped out. She is really too competitive." (You manipulated her out of the group because you are competitive and she got in your way.)

"I don't know what will become of me if he doesn't straighten out. I can't stand it much longer." (You are having the time of your life. If he straightened out, you wouldn't have anything to live for.)

"Let the others push ahead. I'm content just to stay on the sidelines. You know me—always letting others push me around." (You are afraid to tackle anything for fear you will fail. Letting others push you around is a handy excuse for not trying.)

"One thing about me—I'm honest. I always say what I think." (You are tactless and rude, and hurting other peoples' feelings gives you a sense of importance.)

"I love my daughter-in-law, but the poor child doesn't know how to do anything and her cooking is killing my son." (You are jealous of your daughter-in-law, and it would kill you to admit that she is a lot smarter than you were at her age.)

"Well, that is one thing *I* would never do!" (You have never been faced with that temptation. You don't know what you would do. It is easy to defend a fort that has never been assaulted.)

"I would never succumb to the temptation that made him fall. I've been tempted by the same thing myself." (No, but you might succumb to another temptation that *he* would resist).

"I did not commit that sin because my principles are too high." (You did not commit that sin because you were afraid of the consequences.)

"I failed in that job because nobody understood my talents." (You failed in that job because you were lazy.)

"I forgave her for doing that to me because I am a Christian and love her in the Lord." (And don't you feel smug about it? And if you can still talk about the offense, was it really forgiveness after all? And how about loving her for herself too?)

"I like him anyway in spite of his faults." (You like him because of them. His faults make you feel superior. If he did away with them you might not be big enough to like him anymore.)

"I told these friends what she had said to me in confidence because I thought it was for their own good." (Or were you jealous of her and itching to undermine her with these friends?)

Shocking?—these pathetic and sometimes ludicrous examples of self-deception? Not at all, when we apply them to *other* people. Even though we know we have neither the right nor the ability to diagnose the other fellow's motivation, we cannot resist conjecture, for we are all armchair psychologists at heart. It is our *own* blind spots that trip us up, for when it comes to ourselves we do not even speculate, but rather accept the explanation that fits most comfortably and is easiest to live with.

The crux of the whole subject of understanding ourselves and others, hangs on the word "motive." The only way an equitable judgment can be made is to judge the real motive behind the act or attitude, and God reserves that right for Himself. "Therefore judge nothing before the time, until the Lord come, who both will *bring to light the hidden things of darkness,* and will *make manifest the counsels of the hearts*: and then shall every man have praise of God" (I Cor. 4:5). It is not merely that we mustn't; it is that we can't.

I do not discount Christian psychology or Christian psychotherapy. There is nothing like taking tests and seeing yourself laid out objectively and impersonally on a graph, to straighten you out in a hurry. But any good Christian psychologist will be quick to admit that this is only a part of the answer, a start in the right direction—and that the mask, beyond a point, cannot be penetrated. A good psychologist can steer our thinking but only the Holy Spirit of God can probe our bottomless depths, teach us, enlighten us, and pray for us with "groanings that cannot be uttered."

In Bunyan's *The Holy War*, when various Diabolonians were not allowed to be seen in the market square, they hid in cellars and at the opportune time, decided to come out incognito. Bunyan says they "clothed themselves in sheep's russet" to escape detection. Mr. Anger came out as Mr. Good-Zeal. Lord Covetousness, that old villain, called himself Mr. Prudent-Thrifty and was hired by Mr. Mind. There were many more. Those rascals, undetected, kept Mansoul hoodwinked for years.

Now of course we do not go around like ghouls, probing behind every mask we meet, and it would be a morbid thing if we did. In our culture the stock question is "How are you?" and the stock answer— and the only polite one—is "Fine." If you asked me how I was and I told you I had a splitting headache and a trusted friend had deceived me and I was working hard because I had a compulsion to succeed due to the fact that I had been knocked about and over-criticized as a child and that I really wasn't as happy as I looked, I would be a crashing bore.

But the stock answer of "Fine" is never the whole story.

Years ago I was a student in the psychiatric department of a hospital. On my way on duty I went through a surgical floor every morning, and usually in a hurry. One morning a male voice called out to me from one of the rooms and I went back to see what was wanted. He was a young fellow with a most contagious grin, and he told me he had been wondering for weeks what I looked like. "You bounce along with springs in your feet, but you're going in the wrong direction and all I see is your back," he said. "I just wanted to say hello and tell you I've dubbed you 'Happy Feet.'"

Well, we chatted for a moment and I promised him I wouldn't just sail by after that—but would drop in and say hello. I did, every morning. I always said, "How are you?" and he always said, "Fine." But one morning I skidded quickly around the doorway and got halfway into the room before I realized he was not alone. Doctors and nurses were there changing his dressing. I backed out at once, but I had seen.

The bedclothes were down and the dressings were off and there, exposed, was the most horrible X-ray burn. The flesh of his abdomen was completely gone, and there was nothing but membrane between his vitals and the outside world. The doctors were picking off infected pieces of an unsuccessful skin graft. And the stench was beyond belief.

I went on my way, sober and a little sick with what I'd seen.

Next morning I found him bathed and clean and covered again. I greeted him as usual with "How are you?" and he said, "Fine."

But I knew he wasn't fine. For I had stepped into his room in one unguarded moment and smelled a stench and seen a gaping wound that would not heal.

Behind our masks are—if not wounds—inexplicable jungles of hopes and dreams and ambitions and frustrations and losses and fears of failure and all the gnats that plague us; the myriad of things behind masks, good and bad, are legion. Some of them we are aware of. And some of them have slipped into the deep maelstrom of our subconscious to be churned around and around, perhaps never to come to the surface again. And the sum total of them would fill all the books in the world.

We hand God our conscious selves and commit ourselves to Christ and let the deep freeze of our subconscious dangle along as best it can, hoping it won't give us too much trouble by clamoring for attention in devious guises. How many of us have handed over our subconscious to God in so many words? Or prayed for—not the symptom—but the unfathomable *cause* of the symptom—in another?

But that is a subject in itself and too vast to discuss here.

The problem at hand is to remember that what we have seen of another's personality is only a very small part of the total person. He is behind a mask, and if we could only step inside his life in one unguarded moment we might find an ugly gaping wound that will not heal.

"But *I* have wounds too!" we cry. "Don't others realize the same truth about me?" They probably do not. And if they did they might not care. And even if they cared, they might not be able to understand.

We hand our own wounds to God.

CHAPTER 3

CHILDREN ARE NOT DEFENSELESS

Unlike the other chapters, this chapter is not an explanation of how the script therein came to be written. I started out to write it just for fun with no attempt to be serious or prove anything and did not intend to include a script. But as it unravelled, the exercise of prayer in the smallest details of life kept cropping up in my mind, and the story of the Old Man clamored to be told—and so the chapter goes from the ridiculous to the sublime, with no apologies ...

There are a number of fallacies in our culture that we have accepted as fact down through the generations in spite of all evidence to the contrary. Some of them are completely false, and with a reasonable amount of evidence and a little straight thinking can be exposed. The ones that go on fooling everybody are the ones with just enough truth in them to keep people from straight thinking. Our naiveté is appalling. We are taught, for instance, that the animals and reptiles that are endowed with fangs, claws, horns, venom, and various other implements of offensive warfare, can fight. Those who cannot fight can run. And the rest can camouflage themselves to match their surroundings and hide. We are taught that adult humans can use their brawn. Failing this they can use their wits, their money, their ingenuity and their power, to survive. But children are defenseless — totally lacking in brawn, wits, ingenuity and power and all the rest of it.

Now this is a great fallacy. It is one of those partial truths, and we swallow the whole. The part about the children simply is not so.

At one time I did not know it was not so. I believed the whole of it when they laid my first son in my arms. "Poor little defenseless thing," I thought as I cuddled him close. "No wits, no money, no ingenuity, no power, no — "

That's what I thought. Little did I know that he was already making plans. The vague out-offocus stare was only a cover-up. He was eyeing me, sizing me up with uncanny cunning. By the time the nurse took him back he had already concluded: "From a preliminary examination I should guess that handling her should not be difficult. She doesn't look too bright."

Of course he was right. I was very, very dedicated, very, very intense, very, very methodical—and very, very stupid.

He spent ten days in the hospital nursery thinking every minute, and by the time he left for home, he had the groundwork of his campaign laid. It was to be partly offensive strategy, partly defensive strategy, with Plan B ready to go into operation if Plan A failed. And the rest would be purely mopping up operations, with him doing the mopping up figuratively and me doing the mopping up literally.

Once home, the cold war started in earnest. He waged it with methodical thoroughness. He would sleep through his bath, sleep through his cuddle time, sleep through the times he was supposed to move his limbs and get his exercise — in fact, sleep through every hour I was awake working on him and for him. Then when I tumbled exhausted into bed —

"Gas!" he would bellow, And after an hour of floor walking there was, it turned out, no gas. "Pin!" he would shriek. And after a thorough examination there was no pin.

As I was one of the thousands intimidated by the "clock method" (i.e., leave 'em alone and let 'em cry until it's time) that was sweeping the country at the time, he ran into a temporary snag, for I turned a deaf ear to his entreaties after the first few false alarms. But it was only an armed truce. He was not licked. "Gas!" he would bellow, and manage a good-sized belch when I picked him up. "Pin!" he would shriek, and there *was* a pin. So by carefully spacing the legitimate complaints with the trumped-up ones, he perfected the most deadly strategy of all — first wearing down, then confusing his opponent.

The confusion mounted with passing of time. I am a normally intelligent woman who usually learns by mistakes, but as quickly as I would profit by one and vow "never to do *that* again" — he would "never do *that* again" either. He would think up something else. And so I never had a chance to work out what I'd learned.

When his little brother arrived, I vowed that this time it would be different. But when he peeked for the first time inside the little blue bundle and said, "Hello Steve. I'm your brother Gary" — a knowing look was exchanged between them — and an almost imperceptible wink.

In the years that followed I wore out my old psychology text books and trailed the boys with dogged determination, slapping hands rather than removing forbidden objects, and as the wag said, "applying the board of education to the seat of learning" for more serious crimes, like dumping ink into the sugar bowl, ruining the dining room ceiling by flooding the upstairs bathroom, pulling up most of my carrots while they were still embryos, decorating the house with left-over paint, and "driving" my car by releasing the brake and coasting out into the street.

Though I must admit in all honesty that my methods worked, they never worked to my complete satisfaction. There was something wrong, but I couldn't ever put my finger on just what. It was true that they always obeyed after the punishment in that particular area, but they were eluding me somewhere. For instance, they never again ruined the dining room ceiling by flooding the bathroom. They ruined the bedroom ceiling by walking on the unfinished floor of the attic. And they never again pulled up any more carrots. They pulled up soybeans. They obeyed me to the letter. They absolutely never repeated the same crime twice.

In the face of all this I still believed that children were defenseless, lacking in wits, money, ingenuity, power, and all the rest of it. I had no inkling that this was a fallacy. To say it was would be tantamount to saying the earth was flat. You had overwhelming odds against you. The tenacity with which this conviction clung is evidence that I think slowly and am loath to let go of an old idea once it has taken root. It broke down by small degrees, a little chink here and a little chink there.

When a dinner guest once handed them each plastic boats exactly like the ones I'd given them the day before and I gave them a knowing look behind the guest's back and they started to announce that they had boats like that and my look turned from knowing to threatening and they said, "Why are you looking at us like that?" — there was a faint stirring within me. The guest drove them over to the shopping center and exchanged the boats for guns while I was putting the finishing touches on dinner and I thought about that stirring within me and decided it was the first wisp of a suspicion.

As events like that piled up and I found myself mysteriously outwitted time after time, the suspicion began to grow.

It was still growing when we landed at a summer conference one year where I was a speaker. We were in a screened cabin and because the weather was hot we had not bothered to lower the huge shutters that opened upward and were fastened with hooks. Neither had anyone else in the neighboring cabins. Drapes were our only privacy. Vocal privacy was impossible. I had reminded them that they were SK's* as we drove into the grounds. (I learned many years later that that is a grossly unfair thing to do; I did not know it then.) When I perceived our lack of privacy I reminded them again. And *no* nonsense!

*Speaker's kids.

By the second day we had gone through the routine of Don't-do-that and But-those-kids-are doing-it and You're SK's-and-you-can't behave-like-those-kids — and I decided it was time to find out who was boss.

"And this says you can't," I hissed softly, taking a wide belt off a hook, with confidence that the results would be quick and final. They were. Both of them fell to their knees before me, wringing their hands and shrieking dramatically—

"Oh, mother, please, *please!*"

"Don't beat us—please don't beat us!"

"Not the belt, mother, not *that!*"

"Oh *please!*"

I stood, belt raised, stunned to a standstill. Those snub noses, those apple cheeks, those streaming eyes, those crew-cut *monsters* — could they be *mine*? And where on earth did they get all that dramatic ability?

The next moment I was kneeling on the floor too, hissing at them, wiping their noses, imploring them to be quiet and we'd talk it out somehow. We'd settle for no treats for two days instead — or something. They went happily off to play, their tears instantly dry. But then I *knew*.

Poor little defenseless things? No wits? They *lived* by their wits. No ingenuity? When one thing didn't work they had a dozen other ways to go. No power? Ha!

The illusion was shattered, the fallacy exposed

— and I knew at last the meaning of that look they had exchanged when Steve was still just a blue bundle.

I had been the poor defenseless thing with no wits, no ingenuity, no power. From that moment on I was awake. I did not love them any less — just more realistically. And at least *I* had the money.

When a few years later they got jobs in a barbershop shining shoes and I had to borrow four dollars and sixty-three cents from them to pay the milkman, even that last shred of the illusion went quietly down the drain. They had all the rest of those things — and money too. This was a grim business.

I was, as I said, awake to cold reality at last. As the years went on, I was a match for them. Or to put it more accurately, I was more or less a match for them.

I did have my moments of triumph. One of those moments, I remember, sent me into periodic fits of fiendish chuckling for weeks afterward.

They had offered to teach me a jujitsu trick. I was willing to learn, and allowed myself to be led into the living room where there was ample space in front of the fireplace for us to flop about. I wasn't quite sure who was to do the flopping about, but was willing to go along with it. Let the boys have their fun.

One of them was to attack me from behind as

they explained the motions I was to go through to combat it. They went through it in slow motion, explaining each detail with superior patience and the tone of voice reserved for teaching children and adults with low IQ's. I listened humbly and finally we were ready to go. One of them watched while the other one attacked me.

"Now!" said my instructors. "Do it just like we told you." "Like this?" I said meekly — and did it. My attacker flew through the air at an incredible height and with incredible speed. He crashed, sprawling, several feet away. There was an amazed silence. Then we all dissolved into helpless laughter. They patted my back and spoke words of extravagant approbation all the way back to the kitchen.

But nothing more was ever said about teaching me more jujitsu. Whenever the subject came up they looked at me with grave respect.

But I admit to a few moments of panic too.

Like the evening a misunderstanding (understatement) arose and Steve threatened to leave home (dramatics) and I told him to go ahead (bluff and bravura) and the misunderstanding (understatement) was finally resolved satisfactorily in my mind (logic) but not in his (unreasonableness). I went to bed and forgot it.

The next morning I started breakfast and was in the act of spearing a sausage with a fork when I suddenly realized the house was ominously quiet. I went into the boys' bedroom. Gary was away at boarding school so of course his bed was neatly made. Steve's bed was rumpled but empty.

I stood, unbelieving, then with rubber knees, went to the phone. Only the sausage held me up. I leaned on it heavily as I contemplated what to do. My mother? She was three thousand miles away. The police? At that moment the phone rang. It was the mother of Steve's best friend. "Steve's here," she said. "He stayed with Bill last night. Said he had no place to go. That he — that you — "

The sausage wobbled on the end of the fork as I clung to it and burst into a tearful explanation. I leaned on it while I talked with Steve on the phone, and walked the floor with it until he came home. I never did eat it.

One night a few weeks later, I sneaked out to a phone booth and called her back. "Bill's here," I said. She began a tearful explanation. "Don't worry," I interrupted matter-of-factly. "I'll feed him, bed him down and send him home in the morning."

I had learned at long last what somebody should have told me in the first place. Animals and reptiles who are endowed with claws, horns, fangs, venom, and various other implements of offensive warfare, can fight. Those who cannot fight can run. And the rest can camouflage themselves to match their surroundings and hide. Adult humans can use their brawn. Failing this they can use their wits, their money, their ingenuity and their power to survive. Children are lacking in brawn. But they are born fully equipped with built-in wits, ingenuity and all the rest of it — plus a devastating weapon — a great dramatic ability. And they wield a power that defies analysis. They size us up while they're still in the basket, they analyze us, read our minds, anticipate our every move, and neatly and accurately categorize us and calculate their strategy accordingly.

The only way I have ever been able to cope with mine has been by prayer. In *"Pilgrim's Progress,"* after Christian had been outfitted in the armory of the Palace Beautiful with helmet, shield, breastplate, sword and shoes — his hosts took him down a corridor and opened a door and showed him a great secret. It was a closet — and the great secret was prayer. Though his other weapons served him well, it was this great secret weapon that really gave him power. With it he defeated Appolyon in the Valley of Humiliation. And he defeated Giant Despair and his wife Diffidence and escaped from the dungeon. In all the major victories of his life, the tide in battle was turned in his favor when he stopped trying to go it on his own strength and used this most powerful of all weapons.

You may think it astonishing if not appalling that, possessing this great weapon, I did not have the sense to use it more often. But this chapter covers only a very small part of the whole. I have admitted only a few minor mistakes and no victories. Any Christian's total mistakes, were they to be admitted, would require more than a chapter. They would fill books. Christians who do not admit mistakes, untoward attitudes and secret rebellions are very difficult to learn anything from. Partly because they are too good to be true and partly because they are crashing bores.

The truth is, I did use the weapon more often than I did not. Many of our problems were serious ones. It was the days when I awoke at five-thirty and sneaked downstairs to a favorite spot in, of all places, the kitchen — to pray — that I had the upper hand. And later, when the boys were older and I was traveling, it was the nights when, computing the time difference, I would set my alarm for the hour when their day was beginning and pray for them in my hotel room — that things went well. All of which goes to prove that, short of bulldozing a child into trembling submission (and any adult who does that is less than human), you don't stand a chance against his built-in equipment without your complete armor on, all your senses (including a great deal of common sense and a sense of humor, though a sense of the ridiculous is even better) — and the secret weapon.

The children I'm talking about are not the Elsie Dinsmores, but the ones who baffle us, stump us, argue with us using their own peculiar brand of frightening logic, make us weep with frustration, make us laugh, keep us on our toes, and are apparently impervious to our bungling. They manage to survive, in fact, in *spite* of our bungling.

I would like to include a script here that may seem out of place because it has nothing to do with children at all. It does, however, have to do with the secret weapon, reduced to its very simplest form and available to anybody, even the most unschooled in its use.

The portions at the beginning and end are drawn from my own experience in prayer with one of my boys. I have made "Gramma" the narrator.

The meat of the story — the tale of the old man — is adapted from a true account of an unnamed old gentleman of God. It happened somewhere in Scotland. And it is true.

* * * * *

NOTHING'S TOO SMALL...

The woman sat on the foot of the bed, her head bowed, but she was watching the boy praying. He was hunched over the bed, his elbows dug in, his fists pushed in his cheeks, and he was frowning as though in fierce concentration. But his words belied it. They came out in a rush. "And dear Heavenly Father — make me a good boy and bless mother and daddy and sister and my dog and stop all the wars and bless all our plans and help all the people in the world, somehow, amen. What's the story tonight, Gram?"

"Hold on there," she said. But she was smiling. They were friends. "You romped through that prayer like it was a multiplication table."

"Well, I said everything I could think of, and now I'm through."

"You didn't ask Him to help you fix up the trouble between you and Skipper."

"No — well that's different."

"And that little business you've got to straighten out with your Dad. Those are real problems, you know."

"But God isn't interested—"

"In the wart on your nose. Yup, I know. There are two schools of thought on that."

"But He's busy with wars and—"

"Um hm. Wars and nations and kings and a world full of problems. I know that too."

"What do you mean — two schools of thought?"

"That means two opinions. Some think God has time only for big things. That's one school of thought."

"And?"

"And some think He means just what He says — that He cares about every problem, big or little, and wants to be included in every part of your life."

"It's wrong to think He's interested only in big things?"

"Well it's underestimating God. I think when we see God some day, we'll be surprised at all the ways we've underestimated Him." She cocked her head and looked at him a minute. "I've changed my mind about what I'm going to tell you tonight."

"You're not going to tell me a story?"

"Oh yes. Of course. But not the one I'd planned to. I'm going to tell you a story about prayer."

"Oh. Is it a long one?"

"Well, I know two of them. They're about two people who took God at His word. One was an old man — one was a little boy. Which one do you want to hear?"

"Mmmmmm. If I choose one, will you tell me the other one too, sometime?" he bargained.

"Uh huh."

"Mmmmm. Let's see. The old man!"

"All right." She cleared her throat. (she always did; it was part of the ritual) and began:

"Once upon a time there was an old man. He was a very poor old man."

"Ohhhhhh." (That was part of the ritual too.)

"He didn't have much money. But he'd taken the Lord Jesus as his Saviour, and he had the deepest, simplest love for the Lord in his heart. Well. *One* day," — ah, now, the story was beginning — "something very special happened in this old man's life. In those days, life wasn't as fast and exciting as it is now — they didn't have cars and radios and television and planes and things like that. And Christians didn't have the opportunities to hear the Word of God the way they do now. So this was something special. A great evangelist — famous all over the country — was preaching in another town a few miles away. Series of meetings. Everybody was talking about it, and everybody wanted to go."

"And this old man wanted to go!"

"He certainly did. He didn't have a horse and buggy to go in, either, but that didn't faze him a bit. He did up a simple lunch and started early in the morning, hiking along the road."

"It was a long way?"

"Oh *my* yes! Took 'most all day! but he didn't mind. He was used to things like that."

"He went all by *himself*?"

"He started out by himself. He walked a long way, when he was overtaken by a young fellow — and what did they find but that they were both going to the same place."

"To the meetings!"

"Yes—to the meetings. The young fellow turned out to be a seminary student—and so they had a lot to talk about and enjoyed each other's company. And when it came time to eat, they stopped by the roadside and took out their lunches. And they prayed."

"They said grace."

"Uh huh. And the student—*my!* He thanked God for the food in a beautiful studied prayer full of well-turned-out pious phrases he'd learned just so. My, it was a prayer to make a simple fellow tongue-tied, you know."

"Was the old man tongue-tied?"

"Oh no!" she laughed. That old man had lived so close to God, it would take more than a literary prize prayer to freeze him up. When they finished lunch and were ready to start on, the young fellow asked the old man to ask God's blessing on the rest of their trip — 'cause they didn't have too far to go now."

"And the old man prayed," prompted the boy.

"Yes—he prayed for both of them, and for the meetings to come—and then before he finished, his prayer took a turn that made the young student sneak a look at him to see if he were fooling.

"'And Father,' the old man said, 'there's

something special I'd like to ask you. Matter of fact, there are three things. You know I'm hard of hearing—and You know how bad I want to hear that sermon tonight. Now I'm asking You for a front seat. I know it'll be crowded — but nothing's too hard for You. And I know You want me to hear. And then—I need some shoes, and I know You know that too. And oh—! Lord, I need a place to stay too. 'Most forgot. And now, Lord, we'll leave the meeting and the sermon and all our needs in Your hands. In Jesus' Name, amen.' And he turned to the student. 'Well. I guess we'd better move on.'

"And the student was incredulous! 'I say,' he sputtered, 'do you really think that God— that God—'

"'What's the matter?' said the old man, and his eyes were twinkling.

"'Nothing. Only—' The student took a deep breath and began again. 'Only, in all my life I never heard anyone pray for such —for such—in such a manner. Do you really think God will answer a prayer like that?'

"Now it was the old man's turn to be surprised. 'Oh *yes*,' he said, 'He certainly will. You see, He looks past my poor English and my lack of theological terminology.' He chuckled. 'You see I know some big words too.' He cleared his throat. 'And he cares. Don't ever underestimate God. I know.'

"'Well. All right.' The student picked up his things. 'We'd better move along. But I'll be very much interested to find out if—and how—your prayer is answered.'"

The boy laughed. "That *was* some prayer. *Was* it answered?"

"Well, we'll see," said the woman. She had an eager audience now and she was enjoying it. "They went on into the town, and it was even worse than they'd expected. Horses and buggies lined up for blocks away from the church."

"Oh oh."

"Mmmm. And the church was just crowded to the doors. Every seat was taken." They squeezed in anyhow and got into the standing line in the back, and stood there, the old man cupping his hand up to his ear so he could hear—though the preaching hadn't started yet. And they hadn't been there five minutes when an usher came and bent close to the old man's ear.

"'Pardon me,' he said.

'Hm?' said the old man.

'Will you come with me, please? There's a seat for you in one of the front pews.'

'For me? Oh. Well, thank you, sir.' And he said under his breath, 'And thank

You, Father.' Then he turned to the student and said matter-of-factly, 'Well, g'bye, Son. See you after the meeting.'

"And he marched down the aisle into the very front pew, and sat down alongside a most beautiful and well-dressed young lady.

"'Ehhh.' He settled himself with a comfortable sigh. Then he turned his head and whispered. 'Do I have you to thank for this nice seat?'

'Good evening,' she whispered back. 'This is my father's seat. My father said if he wasn't here by seven-thirty, to give his seat to some worthy person. I was looking toward the back for him—and I noticed you standing there with your hand cupped to your ear. Soooo—'

'Well. Well, thank you,' he said, and under his breath, 'Thank *You*, Father.'

"Well—when it came time to pray—the old man was the kneeling-down kind of pray-er, and the young lady was the standing-up kind. And with her head bowed, she couldn't help seeing the holes in the bottom of the old man's shoes."

"She shoulda had her eyes closed, Gram," the boy said.

"This is not time to split hairs," the woman said back quickly. "Anyway, while they were taking up the collection, the young lady leaned over toward the old man and said: 'I hope you won't be offended, but I couldn't help noticing your shoes. You — well, my father owns a shoe store. And — I can get in easily after the meeting. I have a key. Our houseman who drives me home will help us—and we can fit you with a new pair. Will you accept it as from the Lord?'

"Well, he thought about that for a moment. Then he said, 'That's awful nice of you, Ma'am. Yup. Thank you, ma'am. You're awful kind.' And under his breath, 'And thank *You*, Father.'"

The boy was sitting on the bed now, hugging his knees. "Boy oh *boy!*" he said, "isn't that something? Two of his things were answered. Two down. And one to go!"

"Well it *is* kinda exciting, isn't it?" She laughed and shifted her position, savoring what was to come.

"First, they had a wonderful meeting and that old man just listened to God's Word like a—well like in the poem: 'Little children looking up — full of wonder, like a cup.' That's just the way he listened. And when the meeting was over, he passed the young student outside on the church steps, and he called out: 'Good night, Son. See you tomorrow night's meetin'. I'm on my way to the store to get me a new pair of *shoes!*' "

They laughed hard then, the woman and the boy. She slapped her thigh, and he hugged his knees and rocked back and forth. They laughed at the sheer audacity of it, this adventure in trusting.

"Well," she said, "They got to the shoe store and tried on shoes till they got the right pair." She acted it out, thrusting out her foot and examining it.

" 'How do they feel?' asked the young lady.

'Fine,' said the old man. 'Just fine.'

'Walk around a bit,' she said. 'Sure they're all right?'

'Oh, just fine, Just fine and dandy.'

'Well you'd better have two pairs. Rob' —she said to the houseman. 'Rob — will you get another pair the same size please? And wrap them up. Thank you.' She turned to the old man to say good-bye. 'It was nice of you to share my pew in the absence of my father. I've enjoyed your company. And now — can't we drop you off to wherever you're going?'

'Why you certainly—why—ehhhh.' He started several times and then he floundered and stopped.

'What is it?' asked the young lady.

'Why, you see, ma'am, my Father has a room for me, only I don't know—He just hasn't got around to telling me where it is yet.'

'Your fath—ohhhh. Your Father in heaven. You mean God.'

'Yep. God.'

"She looked at him in wonder for a minute. Then: 'Look. Dr. Allen — he was supposed to be our guest all this week to assist at the meetings. He sent word that he couldn't come. So there's an empty guest room at our house. I'— She laughed and held out her hands to him as if they were in sudden conspiracy. 'This is getting monotonous. I hope you won't be offended. Why don't you— *won't* you come and stay with us? We'd— why, we'd be *honored* to have you!'

'Ma'am'— he fished for his handkerchief and cleared his throat. 'This is gettin' more wonderful by the minute. You're just—I'd love to accept your kind invitation, Ma'am. And thank you.' And softly, 'And thank *You* Father.'"

They laughed again, the woman and the boy, but softly this time.

"Well," the woman said, "next night, after the meeting, the old man ran into the young student outside the church.

" 'Hello there, Son,' he said.

'Hello, Sir. Wonderful meetings.'

'Yup. Wonderful.'

'I see you got your new shoes. And your front seat.' They looked at each other for a moment. And then the old man said, 'Ain't you gonna ask if I got my room?'

'No.' The student shook his head. 'Somehow I know you got that room.'

'Yep, son. I did.' They were silent again. Finally, 'Wonderful meetin's, eh?' the old man said again.

'Yes—wonderful.'

'Learned a lot?'

'I learned a great deal more than I bargained for. I—came here to hear an eloquent preacher. So I could study his style and learn great things. But I learned—greater things, Sir.'

'Oh?'

'Yes. I watched your face in the audience and learned how to listen. You weren't listening to a great preacher. You were listening to God.'

'That's right, Son.'

'And I heard you pray and I learned about prayer. You weren't just praying a nice prayer. You were talking to God. You brought heaven down. It—*meant* something. I just want you to know—how rich it's made me—knowing you.' He thrust out his hand and said simply, 'Goodnight, Sir.'

'Good night. And Son'—

'Yes?'

'Just don't ever — underestimate God, Son. Nothing's too hard for Him. Nothin's too small.' Then he turned and shuffled off into the dark."

Neither the woman nor the boy said anything for a moment. Then the boy sighed and stretched his legs out in front of him. "Nothing's too hard for Him. Nothing's too small," he said. "I liked that story. He was a great old man."

"Are you ready to straighten out those problems now?" she said softly, "to really talk with God?"

"Will He do anything I ask Him? It says if I pray in Jesus' name—"

"Do you know what it *means* to pray in His name?"

"I don't know. I don't think I know."

"It means to pray in His nature. To be so identified with Him that you wouldn't pray for anything He didn't already want you to have. Let's do it right now, shall we?"

He scrambled to his knees again. "Dear Heavenly Father," he began. "I wasn't really praying before. Just sorta saying words. You know—" He rubbed his nose. "And I want to fix up what I did wrong today. And I want to ask about—well about a lot of things. First there's . . ."

And he dug his fists back into his cheeks and got down to business.

*****

To say that God is not interested in small "unimportant" details is to vastly underestimate God. And there is no area of your life more replete with infinitesimally small details than the area of your dealings with your children.

You can talk to God about your children. You can tell Him everything, ask Him anything. You can even laugh with Him about the funnier things. I believe He understands laughter. For He is the One Who *made* your children so funny in the first place.

CHAPTER 4

TIME

Oh! What a crowded world one moment may contain!

... F. Hermans, *The Last Constantine*

Perhaps I am the last person in the world to talk about taking time to appreciate the things that go unnoticed in the mad rush of our modern living. Between conference dates and dinner club dates I use up about two hundred air tickets a year, to say nothing of buses, trains and car rentals—and I have eaten my way through enough banquets to stock a good sized commissary with fried chicken and ham and raisin sauce.

But oddly enough, the things I've stopped to relish and the things remembered now are not concerned with travel or excitement or strange places. They are most ordinary incidents and scenes and flashes of scenes of no import at all. I could have the same things to remember and relish if I'd stayed on Elm Street all my life.

I heard a preacher once who in the course of his sermon reported on his first visit to Los Angeles. "We rented a car," he said, "and I piled the family in it and started out for a ride. Our first object was to see the sea, but after we got on one of your California freeways, our only object was survival."

It is the way with life. Things have a way of getting complicated and they pile up on us and we are so confused trying to get them all done that we miss the things of great wealth that are right under our noses.

But once in a while there comes a rare flash of *awareness*, a sharpness of perception and appreciation and gratitude — that seems to make time *stand still* for a moment, and we stop and drink in the experience as if it were the last one we were ever going to have. The pity and the waste of it is that we do not do it more frequently. And often the reason is that those lovely things surprise us in the most unexpected places and moods—when we are rushed or blue or angry or just too preoccupied to notice. Such things, for me, have always been surprises and have come about in the most ordinary ways.

I walked down to the foot of our yard once, clad in boots and groaning under my breath. The yard had not been landscaped yet, the soil was clay, and it had rained all night. Now you have never been bogged down until you have tried to walk in wet clay. I sank in up to my ankles and pulled the boots out like suction cups with every step. I was on a dismal errand, to retrieve sheets and towels and socks and dungarees. The clothesline had broken, scattering them in sullen silence in the muddy clay. We'd had dozens of grassy yards, but no clothesline had ever broken on *them,* I thought. No. The one clothesline that had to break in my whole life, had to break in *this* yard on *this* morning. I was bitter.

By the time I reached the edge of the wooded ravine that bordered the foot of the yard, I was bitter enough to cut the clothesline in inch-long pieces and end its career forever. Any clothesline that couldn't function any better than that didn't deserve a second chance. *Any* clothesline . . . . .

I saw it then. I saw it and forgot to cramp my toes on the next step, and pulled my foot right out of its boot. I hung on to a tree and kept my raised foot in the air and looked.

The ravine ran down into a moss-carpeted glen and the sun dappled it with light. And in the very center was a dogwood tree in full bloom, bent over as if in ecstatic protest that it had all the rain and all the blossoms and all the beauty it could bear. The tenacious raindrops clung to everything, trembling as they clung, and catching the sunlight in a million tiny prisms, and the moss carpet and the dogwood tree and the raindrops seemed to be sharing a secret of shimmering beauty and it was as if a million notes of music hung in the air.

I put my foot down slowly, felt for the boot, missed it, and stood with my bare foot in the clay and watched almost without breathing. What a flagrant extravagance! It was as if God just flung beauty everywhere and anywhere without any thought as to where it was going! It was so quiet down there. Was the dogwood tree bowed down with blossoms and rain, I wondered, or was it bowed down in worship? And for a moment, time stood still, and I worshiped too—until a saucy chipmunk ran across the moss carpet and turned and looked up at me and scolded and broke the spell. I found myself laughing aloud at him, and he scampered away to his morning chores, and I turned away to mine. The wretched clay was still there and the clothes had to be rewashed and the clothesline was still a culprit, but somehow the sting was gone. For I knew where there was a dogwood tree!

There have been other moments when time has stopped and they are all equally insignificant in themselves. It is what they did for my soul that counts.

Like the time I'd just put a bowl of pansies on a cherry piecrust table and our baby kitten settled himself alongside them and tucked in his paws and dozed in the sun and Gary, who could just reach the top of the table, buried his nose in a pansy and said solemnly, "Breath of God." A pumpkin pie in the oven was just beginning to send its spicy promise through the house, and that and the child and the kitten and the bowl of pansies were all mixed up in a sudden sharp awareness of how good God had been to me.

How can we explain these perfectly ordinary things that suddenly make us grateful? They hardly make sense in themselves.

Like the one time I had coffee before church with friends at a garden cafe and we sat at umbrella-sheltered tables outside and the sun sneaked under the edges to warm our backs. The pungent scent of cinnamon toast was mixed with the smell of good coffee, and the talk was talk that would warm your heart. And I detached myself from the talk for a moment and thanked God in my soul for toast and coffee and sun and Sunday mornings and friends and church—and went back to join the conversation with a lump in my throat.

And the time my boys brought two baby goats down from their mountain retreat and told me they were in the car and I didn't believe them. But sure enough they were—two black bambi-like creatures, bundles of riotous good humor and affection—and all legs. Once out of the car, they scampered down the street and the boys called them back and they stopped in tangled confusion and came back gleefully as if pleasing us was the one thing they wanted to do most in all the world. And the boys fed them with nippled baby bottles and they guzzled noisily and the milk clung to their whiskers. And watching, I got another foolish lump in my throat because this was a rare moment filled with good things.

And one Christmas, at the end of a party, there in a gracious living room where my friend Martha spun sheer magic for us on a harp. Now you have never really felt "Christmassy" until you have watched a beautiful woman play Christmas music on a harp. The reflections from the Christmas lights played on her hands as they plucked the strings—and then she began to play the old familiar carols and the guests began to join in until we were all singing softly. And I thought my heart would burst with the beauty of it. It was a moment of sheer enchantment—ephemeral—and time stood still.

Some of the moments you relish, not because they were happy, but because they were tender or because they brought hearts together somehow. Like the time the boys called from outside that our dog had been killed by an auto and when I went out, they were standing there in the rain with a shovel and Teddy's body in a little red wagon they'd borrowed from a neighbor in order to bring him home. We lifted him carefully and brought him up on the porch out of the rain and knelt around him and wept unashamedly, big, salty, therapeutic tears.

But the time I relish the most, and perhaps as much now as I did when it happened, is the time concerned with the story in this chapter. It was back in the Cub Scout days and those days are hectic, as any parent knows. Mornings were especially so, for I was determined to pray with each boy separately and in private. They'd been using their prayers to admonish each other and complain about each other, each one asking God to please straighten the other one out, and our morning prayer time had become almost comic. Separate prayer times seemed the best solution, and it turned out that it was. But it was devastating to the early morning routine and I had to work it out with military precision to get it all done, get each one on his own school bus, and get myself off to a morning radio show. No matter how early I got up or how carefully I adhered to the schedule, an unforeseen problem would arise each morning with unfailing regularity to throw us off.

On this particular morning the problem was a Cub Scout badge that had to be sewn on Steve's uniform. And of course, being a little boy, he had waited until the last minute to tell me about it.

"You mean *now*?" I wailed. "Steve, I simply *can't*."

"But I've *got* to have it on. It's den meeting this afternoon—and right after school!"

"But can't it wait—or be pinned on—or something?" My voice trailed off helplessly when I saw his face.

"All the other kids'll have theirs *sewed* on." He waited hopefully. I wavered.

"I'll baste it on with big stitches for now. It'll do for one meeting. And tonight I'll sew it on right." I was already running for the needle and thread. I sewed it on with silent impatience, and all but pushed him out the door to get his bus. At the gate he turned and grinned. One of his front teeth was missing and I suppose at that time he was the homeliest kid in the state of New York. But something happens to a boy in a Cub Scout uniform. He stands taller and straighter, with an air about him—a sense of grave responsibility. I stood taller too, and grinned back. "Sew it on straight," he called, "with little stitches. So it'll be neat." Then the bus came and he was gone.

I stood at the door and thought, "He will never be that precious or look that funny again." And, "I'm glad I sewed the badge on." And, "It meant so much to him. What if I'd been cross and refused and then he got killed today and I never had another chance?" I made a fervent vow to God that I would do every little job in the future as if it were my last chance to do it. And then I thought of what he'd said—"Sew it on straight with little stitches so it'll be neat." And then I cried.

A bit dramatic perhaps. But a story was brewing. And it takes a bit of doing to brew a story. You feel it first. Then you write it. And after my radio show that morning that is exactly what I did. I wrote it for my weekly Sunday story program. And I called it

* * * * *

I HAVEN'T TIME

They've let me be with you alone for a little while, Son. I had something for you I didn't want anyone else to see, for no one else would understand, and I wanted to be alone with you when I gave it to you—to see if I could make you understand.

They're all so sorry for me and so careful of my grief, but none of them understand.

I wish I knew where to begin. I do not, for I don't know when you stopped being an all absorbing, exciting something new, and started being —

It's hard to explain. One day it's all bottles and formulas and wakeful nights and exhausting days and baby books with all conception of time lost, and the world—the unreal, unimportant world—drifting by. And the next day it's an acute sense of time lost, of youth lost, of strength lost, of confusion, of disappointment. Or at least that's the way it was with me. You weren't anything like I'd thought you'd be, like I'd dreamed you'd be. You were a nightmare of noise and raucous laughter and muddy feet and bad manners and clumsiness and mischief who wouldn't, couldn't learn anything. You were a constant source of irritation.

Tender moments? There were no tender moments. I was too busy. There wasn't time. Tonight it seems as if my whole life hinges on that—there wasn't time. There wasn't time to hold on to precious moments, just to hold on to them while time stood still — knowing their value. There wasn't time to laugh, to love, to discover all over again through your eyes, the wonder of living. The opportunity was there but I never saw it. I never saw it—

Our encounters were never part of the mainstream. They were always interruptions.

"Mommie—hey, Mommie!"

"Where have you been? You're a sight."

"Don and me were frog hunting."

"Don and I."

"And look what we found. He's—"

"Ohhhhhhh! *Kip!*"

"He's only a baby."

"Don't come near me with that thing!"

"He won't hurt you. He's cute."

"He's filthy and slimy. And you're filthy too. Frogs. I loathe them. Put it down under the porch."

"I'll put him in a can. Hey, Mommie— may I — "

"Kip. Not now. I have to go out. To a meeting. And Mrs. McCauley is coming to stay up with you. Come in and get cleaned up. And hurry. And hold your stomach in, Kip, *please.*"

"Mommie, I know where I can get a dog."

"Hurry. And *do* straighten up. Mrs. McCauley—a *dog?*"

"Yes. He's a — "

"No. No dogs."

"He's a beautiful sort of a semi-half-way

93

Collie. Sort of an all-American. I can get him for noth—"

"*No.*"

"I'd take awful good care of him. He loves me. He jumps up on me."

"He'd jump up on everything else too. I hate dogs."

"We can train him!"

"Muddy feet and — *No.* No dogs. That's final. Come on. Hurry. Of all the times to come in late with a harebrained scheme. Kip, come *on.*"

We hurried. Mrs. McCauley came and I went out to my meeting. We talked no more about the dog. I didn't have time.

When you came to me about the Cub Scout business, Kip — I didn't see you — earnest, eager, your two front teeth missing. I didn't stop and treasure the fact that you'd never look quite that funny and precious again. I just saw my clean kitchen floor and the afternoon flying by, and you were an interruption.

"Mommie!"

"Kip, for Lord's sake, wipe your feet."

"Sure. Mommie, could you go for a walk with me? I have to find ferns and leaves and stuff and tell what kind they are, for Cub Scouts. And could you hear me say my Cub Scout oath. To see if I know it? I have to pass a lot of tests and get a badge. Is that a cake?"

"Yes. And you can't have any. It's for a meeting."

"Oh. Could I lick the frosting bowl?"

"I already put it to soak."

"Oh. How about the ferns and leaves and stuff? Could you help me?"

"Oh that. Kip, will you stop just standing there and get a move on? Wash your face and hands and change your shirt if you're going to be around here. I have people coming—"

"But my ferns and leaves and stuff—"

"KIP, I HAVE MORE THINGS ON MY MIND THAN CUB SCOUTS!"

"I thought — I was gonna show you that dog. If you just *saw* him, you'd—"

"And no dog!"

You must have passed your tests—I never asked you about them. I didn't have time. I didn't even stop to think that you must have passed them when you came to me a few nights later—I was reading—

"Mommie—"

"Hm?"

"The Cub Scout badge. Will you?"

"What Cub Scout badge?"

"I told you all about it at dinner!"

"Oh. Will I what?"

"Will you sew it on?"

"On what?"

"On my shirt! I earned it! I told you! It goes on my pocket. Sew it up straight with little stitches, so it'll be neat. Oh. And I earned something else too. An emblem. To sew on my arm. In Bible Club."

"Oh. That's nice. Now goodnight, darling."

"But Mommie—"

"Kip."

"But Mommie, this has to get sewed on, too. It's for learning my verses. They both have to get sewed on."

"Mmmm. That's nice, darling."

"Look, Mommie. I'll show you. There's a verse to go with each page. The black page says you can't go to Heaven unless you know Jesus. Did you know that?"

"I never thought about it."

"Well it's like—if we were both on Long Island. And we wanted to jump across the ocean to Spain. I could jump out farther than you could, but neither one of us would get to *Spain*. For all have sinned and come *short* of the glory of God. D'you see?"

"Uh huh. That's lovely. Now goodnight, Kip."

"But the next page—that's the red one. 'The blood of Jesus Christ, His Son, cleanses us from all sin.' I know them all. And there's one more. 'He that believeth on the Son of God hath eternal life. He that believeth not is condemned already.'"

"Um. Kip, good*night*."

"Mommie. Do you believe?"

"I laid out your—do I believe what?"

"Do you believe in God?"

"I believe there's some sort of a God, yes."

"You have to do more than that. You have to believe what God says. That the Lord Jesus is your Saviour."

"Kip, you're stalling for time."

"You look so pretty by the fire. It turns your face on and off. I wish I could stay up just once and sit by the fire and talk."

"Well, you can't. Kip—Kip. Your little verses are charming. I don't want to be cross. But you *make* me cross. Now goodnight, darling."

You still stood there.

"Kip!" I said.

"Goodnight, Mommie."

You were gone, and I went back to my book, relieved. We didn't talk of the wonderful things you'd discovered. I didn't have time.

The next day you reminded me to sew on your Bible Club emblem and your Cub Scout badge before you went to school. But I hurried you off. I went to an all-day meeting and didn't think of it again at all. I came home, rushed and tired, and hoped you'd be there

97

so I wouldn't have to worry about you because I had plans for the evening.

You were there, all right, looking for me, waiting for me — with some exciting piece of news that just couldn't wait.

You darted across the street to meet me, so quickly, so quickly —

— And then there was the screech of brakes and the crash of glass. . . .

And then they brought you into the house, only it wasn't you. It was never you again —

Oh, my darling, I had to get away from them, from their well-meaning clumsy attempts at comfort, from their philosophical claptrap. You had all the answers, you — knew — God. And in a few hours they will take you away and I'll never see you again. I had to be alone with you.

Kip, I'd give half my life now, if I could have another chance to sit by the fire and talk with you. For you had the truth, and you have gone into the shining and I am left behind in darkness — and I cannot even remember what you said —

Something about "the blood of Jesus Christ." I can't remember the rest —

And "He that believeth on the Son of God—" I can't remember the rest —

They are coming to see if I'm all right.

Kip, I'd give my life to be alone with you

now and they won't let me. Darling. I have your little book. With the colored pages. And the verses, I'll find to go with them. I'll find them and learn them —

Kip. I know you can't see this. It's your Cub Scout shirt. I sewed on your Bible Club emblem. And your Cub Scout badge. I sewed them on straight, like you said, with tiny stitches, so they'd be neat. I had time, Kip. I have all the time in the world. . . .

* * * * *

I mentioned that I relished this flash of awareness as much now as I did when I wrote the script. And I do, for this past Christmas I sewed something on Steve's uniform again, only this time it was an army uniform. He was home on leave and about to embark for Germany. And I thought as I sewed it on, that they were both gone now, the house was empty and I would never have another chance to make time stand still while I captured a moment of awareness — at least not with them. Everything to be done for them was done. He interrupted my thoughts. "Sew it on straight with little stitches," he said tenderly, "so it'll be neat." And we both chuckled, but the lump in my throat was *something* to swallow.

Most of the jobs we have to do in life are little ones. And much of life centers around the humdrum. You don't have to travel far and do the unusual to find something to appreciate or a job to do with pride.

I think Christ centered his life around ordinary things to show us that it could be done nobly. He was born into the home of a carpenter, brought up in the shadow of a carpenter's shop, worshiped quietly in the neighborhood church, increased in "wisdom and stature, and in favour with God and man" by being faithful in humdrum things. And even in manhood when His ministry became far-flung and exciting and He was famous, He found His greatest pleasure in the fellowship of ordinary people. And in all His life He probably never traveled beyond the radius of 70 miles. And within that radius He met Bartimaeus and made him see, calmed the storm and caused Peter to walk on the water, met the lame man and caused him to walk, raised Lazarus from the dead, showed Nicodemus the way of eternal life, met Zacchaeus and turned his life upside down, cured the demoniac, healed the centurion's servant, fed the five thousand, and as John said, "And there are also many other things which Jesus did, the which, if they should be written every one, I suppose that even the world itself could not contain the books that should be written."

Christ took time to be quiet, to appreciate and

relish a golden moment, to be grateful to God. He never hurried. His Word admonishes us against frantic haste and encourages us to meditate on the good things of God and to be grateful.

The woman in the story finally remembered the golden moments and sewed the badge on "up straight with little stitches, so it would be neat." She had all the time in the world. But it was too late. One of the most bitter tragedies in the Christian's life is to let those moments go by unnoticed and unappreciated — and to bring God jobs finally completed — too late.

Things do have a way of getting complicated and they pile up on us and we are so confused trying to get them all done that we miss the things of great worth that are right there about us. Our flashes of awareness and appreciation of golden moments are too few. But the golden moments fly and if they are not relished they never come back again to give us another chance. I relished a few. I wish now that I had relished more.

CHAPTER 5

A MERRY HEART

All who joy would win must share it—
Happiness was born a twin ...
                              ... Lord Byron, Don Juan
A merry heart maketh a cheerful countenance
                              ... Proverbs 15:13
Teach me half the gladness
That thy brain must know ...
                              ... Shelley, To a Skylark

I think the story in this chapter was born one Sunday afternoon when the boys and I were having dinner at a mountain lodge. I had left a message at the desk, as I expected a friend to phone me and had told him where I would be. We were just beginning our soup when I was called to the phone. Both boys scraped their chairs back and leapt to their feet when I arose, a display of gallantry that gave me a bit of a jolt and prompted me to go whole-hog and say, "Will you excuse me, please?"

When I went back to the table, they were engrossed in conversation, but when they saw me coming they leapt up again, and with more scraping of chairs got me and themselves seated.

This all gave me a strange feeling of unreality. I looked at them with new eyes. Could this mean that all my years of training were, at long last, bearing fruit? Was I dreaming? Could it be — it *was*! They were dipping their spoons away from them! Down through the years I had said:

"Like little ships put out to sea

I dip my spoon away from me."

But without success. After the twentieth time they would join in and repeat it mechanically along with me. They knew the poem, but the connection between the poem and its application escaped them somehow. And now here they were, dipping away as if they'd been doing it all their lives.

As if this were not enough of a shock, the con-

103

versation took several interesting twists and I realized they were cognizant of what was going on in the world, had some serious views of life — and in passing, I noticed that they were even pronouncing their participles. I looked at them with their clean necks, their hair plastered down with alarming neatness, their fine manners, and felt like somebody else. And, like Jane in the following story, the years turned back. Not categorically, of course. The events that flashed through my mind were haphazard and unrelated.

My first ideals and ideas about parenthood, for instance. I tackled motherhood with a fantastic thoroughness that appalled my friends, alarmed my poor mother, and all but finished us off. My sterile efficiency was enough to make any discriminating baby roll up his personal accouterments in a diaper and leave home. Surely the uncertain fortunes of the world could not be worse than the certain misfortune of being in the hands of this grim woman who lived with one eye on her offspring and the other on the clock, and ate lunch with a child-psychology textbook propped against the coffee decanter — probably searching for a paragraph that would tell her it was proper to boil infants for twenty minutes if they got exposed to germs.

As I see it now, the basic problem was my absolute lack of flexibility. At this age of development, if we were on page thirty-six, we had better *be* on page thirty-six. If they were on page thirty-five or thirty-seven, it was a horrible reflection on my ability as a mother and could not be tolerated. And so we lived by pages and chapters. We lived by the thermometer too, until the day I phoned our doctor for the impossible-drillionth time and reported a temperature of 101 and asked him what I should do and he said wearily, "Break the thermometer."

Fun moments? Of course. Saw-horses hitched to the back porch, to be leapt on at a moment's notice to gallop over the plains and carry a secret message to the king. Or to gallop to a secret hide-out (converted piano box at the foot of the yard) to eat lunch. And sometimes lunch eaten while the three of us solemnly wore paper rabbit ears and called each other Flopsie, Mopsie and Mother Cottontail — so the wretched dreadful carrots would go down. And stories. Millions of them. All the Bible stories. And a continued story concerning the adventures of a certain Gary Wayne Sinkstopper and Stephen Paul Wastebasket — that literally ran for years.

But it is not the successful times I want to talk about, for we do not tend to learn from success — and we do not identify ourselves with, or expect any understanding or help from a paragon of success. Success *inspires*, to be sure. But it is from our failures — and other people's failures — that we really learn.

But back to the mountain lodge — and the story.

Other memories in the flash back that day crept into the story. Gary's sliding down the banister and landing with a resounding thud on the back of an unsuspecting guest who was standing in the hallway. The dismal failure of attempted piano lessons. Report cards.

And then a various assortment of oddities that did not get into the story but contributed to its flavor. Steve's being introduced to a distinguished guest and unexpectedly standing on his head instead of shaking hands.

Oh. And the day we were swimming at a conference in the east. We went through the you-can't-do-that-but-the-other-kids-are-doing-it-but-you're-a-speaker's-kid-you-can't-behave-like-those-other-kids routine. So Gary did it. He went down the waterslide head first and plunged head down through the water, sinking himself like a fence-post into the lake bottom. They laid him on the beach, and a preliminary examination by the camp doctor disclosed a possible fractured vertebra. Gary cut his teeth on medical terminology and was not fooled for an instant. "I've got a broken neck," he shrieked. Now a broken neck for some reason sounds more ominous than a fractured vertebra. It suggests the head hanging off to one side.

So it was a solemn and sober little party that entered the ambulance for the fifty mile ride to the nearest hospital. The ride, it turned out, was fun in a weird sort of way. To see the cars ducking and scurrying off to both sides of the road in response to the ambulance siren gives an odd sense of power and exhilaration. I had trouble with my driving for weeks afterward. I still thought I had the undisputed right of way.

As Gary could not raise his head, I gave him my vanity case mirror so he could see the fun. He was beginning to enjoy the whole thing.

The attention lavished on him at the hospital was something to behold. Gary was almost disappointed to find his neck wasn't broken after all. There was nothing wrong that five days of traction didn't fix up.

Back at the conference, we went through the youcan'tdothatbuttheotherkidsaredoingitbutyou'rea speaker'skidyoucan'tbehavelikethoseotherkids routine again. But he didn't do it. He was just sounding me out — a thing I understand is a compulsion in small boys.

And then there was Steve's broken leg. Done in a most undramatic way. A falling truck tailgate. Humiliating. If a boy is going to crack a bone, he wants a tale of derring-do connected with it — something you can get your teeth into. But this was a simple fracture. And suffered in an ignoble way. Like the time he knocked all his front teeth out — not by smashing an athletic record or getting attacked by unknown assailants — but simply by falling up the marble steps with a bag of groceries outside our apartment.

But back to the leg. A temporary cast was put on it, and a week later we went to a specialist where I encountered some of the unfathomable mysteries of orthopedics. The young lady who took the case history was efficient enough, but I could not follow her thinking.

"How old are you?" she asked, looking at me.

"He's the one who broke his leg," I faltered.

"Sixteen," Steve said promptly.

"No, you," she said. So I told her, though I could not imagine why.

"Are you left or right handed?" she fired at Steve.

"But it's his leg that's broken," I ventured.

"Left," said Steve.

It was some time before we got around to the leg, which was what I'd thought we'd gone in for. By the time the great white father appeared, the young lady had me thoroughly cowed and confused, which is what I understand they do to people who enter their portals too self-assured. It's a sort of brainwashing.

We followed the great white father down a very slippery corridor. It had been waxed to a fare-you-well. I nearly lost my footing twice. "With this floor you should drum up extra business. Ought to average two extra fractures a week," I quipped with the uncertain little laugh of a person who has just been thoroughly cowed and confused. He did not answer. He had no sense of humor.

Once in the examination room he looked at the case history with my age on it and said dryly to Steve, "Well, young man, for your age you're in remarkably good condition."

I brightened at once. He *did* have a sense of humor. And that woman in the front office wasn't so bright after all. Ha.

A week later I went off on tour leaving the boys safely boarded in the mountains. Steve's cast was no drawback at all. He had circumvented all obstacles and could do just about anything. For the first week I was only a few hundred miles up the coast and we exchanged letters. But before I took off for New York I thought a phone call was in order. I talked to them both at once.

"How are you," I said.

"I'm okay," said Steve.

"He's okay," said Gary.

"How's everything at camp?" I was still trying.

"It's okay," said Steve.

"It's okay," said Gary.

"Well, I'm off to New York," I offered. "D'you think it's safe for me to go?"

"That's okay," said Steve.

"That's okay," said Gary.

"Are you *sure* you're all right?" I persisted.

"I'm okay," said Steve.

"He's okay," said Gary.

"Well all right then. Goodbye," I said. "You're sure you're okay?"

"I'm okay," said Steve.

"He's okay," said Gary.

"Except for the rattlesnake bite," said Steve.

"Rattlesnake?" I gasped. "Did you say rattlesnake?"

"Yeah. But I had an anti-snake shot at the clinic," said Steve.

"Yeah. He swelled up and turned blue but now he's okay," said Gary.

"Yeah. Now I'm okay," said Steve.

"Are you *sure*?" I was breathing hard.

"Yeah. He's okay," said Gary.

"I'm okay," said Steve. "Except I shot myself."

"Yeah," said Gary. "Tell her how you shot yourself."

"You WHAT?"

"Yeah," said Steve. "It was on account of the rattlesnake. I pulled the gun out to shoot him. But I didn't get it out of the holster fast enough. It's only a flesh wound. I had a tetanus shot at the hospital. It's okay."

"Yeah. He swelled up and turned blue but now he's okay," said Gary.

The silence that followed was punctuated by my heavy breathing.

"Why didn't you tell me?" I said in low measured tones — an effort to control myself. "We've been talking for five minutes. Why didn't you tell me? I *asked* you a dozen times how you were."

"It all happened to the *other* leg," said Steve.

"You didn't *ask* me about the leg it happened to."

I admonished them to hang on and be brave and I would try to get a seat on the next plane back. But they were surprised.

"I'm okay," said Steve.

"He's okay," said Gary.

And I might add in passing that they haven't changed. Only a few weeks ago, there was a phone call from Steve from his army training base. Gary had dropped in for a visit and picked up an extension, so we had a three-way conversation again:

"Look, Mom. You'll be getting a report from the army hospital. But don't worry. I'm okay," said Steve.

"What *is* it?" I wailed.

"Stuck my head out of tank five feet away from another tank that was firing," he said.

"Take it easy, Mother," said Gary.

"Were you hit?" I said, which for obvious reasons was a stupid thing to say.

"Mot*her*," he said wearily. "If I'd been hit I wouldn't be here. Knocked my helmet off and knocked me back into the tank. Banged my head against the side. Got a concussion, that's all."

"And you're out of the hospital now?" I asked. "Are you *sure* you're all right?"

"I'm okay," said Steve.

"He's okay," said Gary.

But back again to the mountain lodge. We finished dinner, they calculated the tip, paid the bill, helped me into my wrap, helped me into the car — all with impeccable finesse — and we went on our way. I looked at Steve. "You're okay," I thought. And at Gary. "You're okay," I thought. And at our life together. "It's okay," I thought. And I went home and wrote

❖ ❖ ❖ ❖ ❖

CHARLEY

Jane and Aunt Agatha walked down the center aisle of the large church, got their programs and were ushered down front into one of the finest pews. The church was already well filled — Jane resisted the temptation to look back up and see if the balcony was filled too; she settled down next to Aunt Agatha to wait for Charley. As she waited, she thought on Charley — which was a pretty big order, for Charley was something to think on. And as she thought, the years turned back.

Of course it had been apparent from the beginning that Charley was a very unusual child. At least it had been apparent to Jane. Things had started out well enough, except for the fact that he'd been named Charles after his father — which was the last thing she should have done, for it led inevitably to the "big Charley, little Charley" business, to avoid "Junior." But other than that, he was off to a good start, an absolute cherub. When a nurse had first brought him into her hospital room, Jane had looked him over carefully and decided he was quite above average. And her mind buzzed with plans for the new chapter in her life.

Jane was a very methodical person, who believed that if you added two and two you had to get four. It was simply a matter of cause and effect, knowledge and application — so she fortified herself with books and more books on the care and feeding of children — and also a shelf of psychology books. She was prepared for anything.

Any resemblance between Charley and the baby in the book, however, was purely coincidental. For he had a most decided mind of his own. Jane insisted that it was a matter of deciding which category he fell into, and the rest would be easy. There was only one catch to that. Charley didn't seem to fall into any category at all. By the time she'd decided he was something no psychologist had ever written anything about, the pre-school years were over. Jane's hopes went up again when she deposited him in school; perhaps the teachers would discover just how he was above average — but she waited in vain for the good news. In school — and in Sunday school — Charley was utterly, utterly average.

Sunday school. It was Charley who went to Sunday school first, and Jane could never think of it without a tightening of her throat in gratitude, all over again. For it was Charley who'd come home from Sunday school with a little wordless book.

"Now. It's a story without words, see."

"Uh huh."

"So — ah — here's — First. The golden page. Do you know what that stands for? That's heaven. 'In My Father's house are many mansions. If it were not so I would have told you. I go to prepare a place for you — '"

"Where'd you learn that?"

"That's in the Bible."

"Hmm. Well. Go on."

"Well. That — that is heaven. Would you like to go there when you die?"

"Well. I expect I will."

"No, Mother. That's just it. You won't."

"Why?" She was half amused, half taken aback.

"Now that's just what I wanted you to ask, on account of here — there, now, that's the next page. It's all black."

"So it is."

"That's *you*."

"Heey now, wait a *minute* — " This was getting a bit thick.

"I'm — I'm not telling you you're black. God tells you you are. You're not going to argue with Him, are you?"

"No — I guess I won't." She settled back, wary now.

"Well. 'For all have sinned and come short of the glory of God.' Now that says that — in the Bible. For *all* have sinned and come short of the glory of God. That means you too, Mom."

"That means me too. Go on."

"Now there's a red page. The blood of Jesus Christ, His Son, cleanses us from all sin."

"The blood of Jesus Christ." She was listening now.

"And here's a white page. 'Wash me and I shall be whiter than snow.' That — that's the only way, Mother, you can get to heaven. D'you see?"

Yes — wonderfully, miraculously, she had seen. It had always amazed her that she had seen. And she had found this Jesus — and had claimed His righteousness for her salvation. In the simplest possible way. She had walked into God's arms like a child. She'd gone to church first. Then to Sunday school. It was a new chapter. No, it was a new life.

And then big Charley had seen it. They'd had two wonderful years.

And then big Charley had died.

That was when Aunt Agatha had moved in, had come to tide Jane over for a month, and had been there ever since. Jane pressed against her gratefully in church, as she thought of it. Agatha had stayed ever since, and ever since, little Charley had been leading them a merry chase.

"But you stood up there on the platform and didn't open your mouth. What was the matter?"

"I don't know."

"Your whole class recited the Scripture. You know that Scripture."

"Sure. 'Put on the whole armor of God, that ye may be able to stand against the wiles of the devil. For we wrestle not against flesh and blood, but against principalities, against powers, against the rulers of the darkness of this world, against — '"

"Why didn't you say it?"

"Hm?"

"Why didn't you *say* it — when you were up there with the class?"

"I dunno."

"And you knew the song?"

"Sure." He began to sing it, all stops pulled out. "A call for loyal soldiers comes to one and all — soldiers for the conflict — soldiers for the — "

"Why didn't you sing it when the rest of them did?"

"I dunno."

"Oh *brother*."

Of course with Charley, it could never be said that two and two actually made *four*. But then it could never be said that there were many dull moments.

"Don't know why I have to practice this foolish thing. Fellows don't play pianos. Fellows don't — "

"Charley — "

"Fellows just don't. The name of this foolish thing is 'A Happy Farmer Coming Home from Work.' "

"Charley — "

"So if he doesn't have to take piano lessons he oughta be happy."

"Charley, stop muttering."

"Hm?"

"You have that wrong, darling."

"I can't hear you. I'm practicing."

"You sound as if you're playing with your elbows — in the cracks. With all those keys on the board, why do you play in the cracks?"

"I don't see why I have to practice this foolish thing. Fellows don't — "

"You're going to sit there and practice until

you get that thing straight. You're going to — "

"The phone's ringing. The phone's ringing."

"You're going to — "

"Phone's ringing. Phone's — "

"I hear it. Keep on practicing. I'll be back."

Hap - py Far - mer — "

"Whslth gldhs dnehd helse kejs!"

"What?"

"Whslth gldhs dnehd helse — "

"WHAT?"

"Will you stop that foolish thing for a minute so I can hear who's on the phone?"

"Ohhh. First I have to practice this nice piece and then I have to stop this foolish thing. First it's a nice piece and then it's a — "

"Charley. It wasn't the telephone. It was the doorbell."

"My piano teacher?"

"No. It's the new pastor. Will you run upstairs and wash your face?"

"I already washed it on the side my teacher sits. She sits — "

"You-get-up-stairs-and-wash-it-on-both-sides-and - your - hands - too - and - your - hands - have - BACKS!"

"Okay, oKAY."

Smile now, she thought. Let pastor in. Keep smiling. Kids will be kids. And Charley is the only kid you have.

"Well, Dr. BAILEY! Of ALL people! How

good of you to call. Come in!"

"Hello, Mrs. Martin. I thought I'd drop by and — ooooof!"

Oh *no!*

Must keep head. Don't blow top. Send Charley upstairs with firm and objective dignity. Help Dr. Bailey up. Help him up. There, that's it. You're doing fine. Don't blow top till he leaves. That's it, hold it till he leaves. Will he *ever* leave? Will he ever — no, please God, let him stay. If he leaves now, you will kill Charley. Let him stay till you cool off. You must not even think of killing Charley. You must not think of Charley. If you stop thinking of the whole business, maybe it will go away. Must keep head. Must — Oh. He's going. At long last. He's gone. Now.

"Charley? You may come downstairs now. He's gone." Ah. You are deadly calm. He stayed long enough.

"Mother. I'm awfully sorry."

"Why did you have to slide down the banister?"

"I guess you didn't hear me coming."

"Why did you have to slide down the banister?"

"You always tell me I make too much noise when I walk down. I thought I'd come down quietly."

"But why did you have to — "

"HOW'D I KNOW HE WAS STANDING RIGHT THERE AT THE FOOT OF THE STAIRS? I THOUGHT YOU'D INVITE HIM IN THE LIVING ROOM!"

For the most part, the rest of Charley's boyhood was one big blur to Jane. Bits and fragments came back to her, plucked from nowhere.

"How do I look, Mom?"

"Mmmm. Wonderful."

"Pretty snappy, hm?"

"Mmm. Pretty snappy."

"D'you think she'll like me?"

"I'm sure she will. Do you have your money?"

"Uh huh."

"Corsage?"

"Yup."

"And don't forget — hey — wait a minute! Your neck is dirty!"

Some of the fragments were of no significance —

"So, Mom. There it is."

"Charley! I never thought I'd live to see this day."

"Yeah. I'm pretty smart after all."

"Oh I never doubted *that* for a minute. But an A in English! Were there many others who got A's?"

"Nope. Just me and two other guys."

"Oh good grief."

And some of them were milestones.

"I learned some stuff in manual training today. I'm going to be real helpful around the house, Mom. I learned how to change a — fix a — put on a new — eh — thing. Washer. Fits the water tap."

"Hm? Well."

"Well. I'm going to fix these — we've got — we've got two drips in the house."

"Three. Aunt Agatha's with us."

"No, you know what I mean. I mean faucets. I've learned to fix 'em. And that's just what I'm going to do."

"Oh oh."

"Hm?"

"Nothing darling. I think that's wonderful. Where're you going?"

"Down the cellar. I have to turn the main water off."

"You *do*?" Keep calm. Show confidence.

"Sure. You have to do that. Gimme a light, will you?"

"Please may I have a light."

"That's what I said. Gimme a light, will you?"

Don't follow him down there. Turn on the light and leave him alone. That's the only way he'll learn —

"Do you know how to do it?" Shouldn't have said that.

121

"Sure. I know how to do it. I know where the place is. I'll just have it off for a few minutes. I've got this down pat. I know how to do it."

He knows how to do it. Leave him alone. That's the only way he'll —

"You just — twist — this — uh — kinda rusty — just — uh Mom! I busted something! There's water — "

Oh *no!*

"Water! Oh *boy!* Can't stop it! Mom, call a plumber!"

Quick. Call a plumber. Easy now. Yellow pages. Can't he do *anything* right? Plumber, plumber, plumber, plumber. Oh brother. Don't get angry. You can't think when you're angry. You won't find a plumber if you get angry. Find a plumber and *then* get angry. Plumber, plumber. Send Charley off to camp. Or away to school. Plumber. Here we are. No, leave Charley home and *you* go off somewhere. Anywhere. Why doesn't he answer? That cellar will be half full before he —

"Yes? Plumber?"

Now. Easy does it. The leak's fixed. The cellar's bailed out. It could have been worse. Charley could have — No. Don't think of Charley. Think of something else. Go talk to Agatha. Find Agatha. Agatha —

"That settles it, Agatha. He isn't my child —

he can't be. They switched babies on me in the nursery, that's what they did, Agatha."

"Well, don't act as if the world had come to an end, Jane."

"But Agatha — he turned — he broke something down the cellar — they've got the water off on the whole street now — "

"Well what of it? It isn't a matter of life or death."

"Matter of life or death? It practically is! It's Monday morning. Everybody's washing. I'll — I'll have to go down the street with a bag over my head for a month. I won't be able to face anybody. And all because he wanted to change a — fix a — put on a washer. What is the matter with that boy? Agatha — where have I failed? Where *have* I failed? What can I *do* with him?"

"If you'd just talk to him more — try to reach his mind — "

"He doesn't have a mind!"

"Oh, Jane!"

"He doesn't have a mind, Agatha. If I could look inside his head, it would be filled with little pebbles. I know it would."

"Jane — calm yourself!"

"Calm myself! Agatha. Other people's children don't act like that. They — they — grow up normally. They — they — they go through from Sunday to Monday — normally. They're *normal.* He starts the week on Wednesday and lives it toward both ends. There simply never *was* another boy — as — as crazy as he is."

"Nonsense. There are at least ten million mothers in this country alone who would throw up their hands in protest if they could hear you say that."

"Well I'll bet you one thing. I'll bet — Oh. Hello, Charley. I didn't hear you come in."

"Hello, Mom. Hi, Aunt Agatha."

"Hello there, Son."

"I'm awfully sorry, Mom. They'll have it fixed in a little while. The place where I went to turn it off was old. It was — kinda rusty. It just — snapped. I'm sorry. *You* know I'm sorry, Aunt Agatha."

"Of course you are. You certainly didn't do it on purpose. It isn't anything that can't be fixed anyhow. So there's no great harm done. The mail is here. You've got some pamphlets from some colleges. Christian colleges, Charles. Have you been writing to them?"

"Yeah. I — sorta — gotta start thinking about the rest of my education. You know. After I get out of high school. What's the matter, Mom?"

"You mean you've been thinking?"

"Heh. Sure. Thinking about what I want to be. What's the matter?"

"Oh nothing. It — just never occurred to

me that you—that you wanted to be *anything*."

"Aw, *sure*. Heh. Mom, I — I want to be a minister. Didn't you *know?* Mom. What's the matter?"

She saw him then, suddenly, at just that moment. Charley. Charley the *person*. Why he was — he was *him*. He was looking at her, his eyes vulnerable, pleading with her to recognize him. She stood in the doorway and they looked at each other. And a revelation came, sharp, sudden, stinging her eyes. And in that moment she lost her child. This person was a stranger. But ineffably dear. She longed to know him. She *would* know him. He was worth knowing.

"Aw, Mom, you're crying. Mom. Don't cry. Mom. Where're you going?"

She did not cry. She laughed sheepishly instead. It was better. "I'm — going to burn up — throw out — some — a — collection of old books I've had hanging around. Psychology books. Stop chuckling. *Both* of you!"

She chuckled again, sitting there in church, thinking of it. Agatha's whisper brought her back with a jolt.

"Jane — Jane."

"Hm?"

"Isn't that Dr. Thornton over there? He's nodding to you, dear."

"Where? I can't see him without my glasses."

"Well nod anyway, you goose. Over there."

"How do you do, Dr. Thornton." She mouthed it, and nodded.

"They're about to begin, dear." Agatha settled back and drew a big breath and it came out trembling. "This is going to be a big evening for all of us. Charles' ordination at last!"

An impressive looking procession filed out on the platform and there — was Charley. Jane caught her breath. There was Charley — tall — incredibly impressive — and his neck was clean!

"Nod back to him," Agatha said. "He's smiling at you."

Jane's throat was getting alarmingly tight. "Is he?" This would never do.

"Yes. Nod."

"I can't — see him."

Her eyes were blurred. He had been her little boy, and now — this! She hadn't prayed enough, she hadn't understood enough, and — most of all — she hadn't *laughed* enough. And yet God had been faithful. Oh, God had been good! She reached over and squeezed Agatha's hand. Yes — all in all — she'd got far better — than she deserved . . .

Now I must confess that the funniest incident in that story — the disastrous attempt to fix the "drip" — did not happen to us. It happened to my nephew Donald. And I might add he turned out very well. He's a brilliant college professor today and working on his doctorate — and did it all on scholarships! But as I said before, stories are drawn from the sum-total of the author's experience. And I have rich funds to draw on.

Charley was written mostly for fun. But if there was one admonition I did want to sneak in, it was that we — or at least many of us — do not laugh enough. We bring our children up with deadly seriousness, with a welter of charts and graphs, comparing them with the "norm" and looking at them with a jaundiced eye if they do not hit it. We lose sight of the fact that there *is* no norm.

Don't compare your child with other children — or with page thirty-six. Look at them and it, if you will, but don't compare. Your child is *your* child — not somebody else's child or the child on page thirty-six. He is the sum total of his genes and chromosomes and his environment. He is *"him."* Accept him as he is, God bless him, and don't try to make him someone else. Is he slow to learn? Edison was sent home from school because he apparently could not learn anything. Does he seem to have a pattern of failure? Abe Lincoln's whole life was pattern of apparent failure until he became president. On the human side, a sense of humor is one of the best traits you can have for parenthood. It smooths out the rocky places.

The serious should not be discounted of course.

We are told that "Foolishness is bound in the heart of a child; but the rod of correction shall drive it far from him" (Prov. 22:15).

But the Bible also tells us that "A merry heart doeth good like a medicine" (Prov. 17:22).

And Christ Himself enjoyed sociability and fellowship. I am inclined to think He enjoyed merriment too, at the proper times and places. And I suppose that is, after all, the crux of the whole problem. In Ecclesiastes we are told: "To every thing there is a season, and a time to every purpose under the heaven: . . . A time to weep, and a time to laugh; a time to mourn, and a time to dance . . ."

If we can discern the proper time for seriousness and the proper time for laughter — and get the correct ratio — we have, with prayer, an unbeatable formula from the Word of God. And the Word of God gives us the blessed, therapeutic, heart-warming privilege of merriment to relieve the tension, add spice to the humdrum, and alleviate the deadly serious business of being a parent.

Laughs? We had a million of them. But, looking back, I can see where we could have had a million more. Alas, we did not. And the fault is mine.

CHAPTER 6

BROKEN SWORDS

*The trenchant blade, Toledo trusty,
For want of fighting was grown rusty,
And ate into itself, for lack
Of somebody to hew and hack.*
                . . . Samuel Butler, *Hudibras*

There is an old fable about a soldier in battle who broke his sword and looked at it a moment in horror and disbelief — then threw it to the ground and fled in panic to the edge of the battle where he could hide. Then along came the prince, who had lost his sword, and seeing the broken sword on the ground, he scooped it up and went on to lead the army to victory.

I approach the subject of handicaps humbly, for I have never known the terror of a broken sword, and many a handicapped person would laugh me to scorn for trafficking in a territory in which I've never had to test my mettle. I am sorry for that soldier; I am not at all sure that I would not have fled in panic too. The world is full of people who have.

But I want to talk about some people who did not flee, but scooped up the broken pieces and went on to victory. I cannot tell you what I would do. But I can tell you what they did, for they crossed my path and left me ashamed that with a whole sword I had not shown greater valor in the battle.

One was a student at a Christian college. His name was Lefty. He called on me when I first moved there — just to welcome me and let me know he'd be glad to take the boys to the park any time and while away an hour or two; he often went over there to study. His speech was slightly slurred and his sight was poor, and when he walked away I noticed his gait was unsteady, too. But his brief visit had somehow left us all feeling better. We had never seen such an abundance of enthusiasm and good humor packed into one person. He had a completely artless charm about him; he was contagious — there is no other word for it. You "caught" him like the measles. My boys adored him.

And then I discovered that everyone else on the campus adored him, too. Not from pity because he was handicapped, but because he was such good company — because he was utterly without guile — and I suppose because he could laugh at himself. He was above pity — he was too happy.

One day Lefty went down to the City Hall to see the mayor because a huge banquet was in the offing for the dedication of a new auditorium, and Lefty thought the mayor might like to come. It never occurred to Lefty that the mayor might not like to come; he was just being neighborly and didn't want to leave the mayor out of such an important event. Now everybody knows that nobody can get in to see a mayor just because he takes it into his head to do so; but Lefty charmed his way past all the red tape and saw the mayor with no trouble at all. You can see the boy was practically hypnotic. "We thought you might like to go to that banquet, your honor," he said cheerfully. "You ought to get acquainted with us and see what we're doing. If you'd go to that banquet and say a few words to us, you'd make seven hundred students awfully happy. We'd be so proud to have you to ourselves for an evening."

And although the mayor was of a different faith, he was so startled he accepted at once. Everybody was amazed at what Lefty had managed to accomplish, but he took the acclaim matter-of-factly, in fact in mild surprise, as if students invited mayors to banquets every day. He was one person in a thousand who could do something like that without being presumptuous. Much of his charm was his unmitigated cheerfulness. It wasn't a pose. He was cheerful from the bottom of his soul up and it was completely irresistible.

I met him years later at a rally. He came up from the audience to speak to me. Or rather his wife came up to say hello for both of them. Lefty didn't have the strength to walk that far and get out to the car, too — so I went down to the back of the auditorium to say hello to him. He held out his hand and grinned from ear to ear, and not a whit of the old effervescence was gone and he never mentioned that the disease that plagued him was getting progressively worse. That was no news anyhow; he had known from the first that it would. But it hadn't kept him from college. Or from looking for folk to talk to about God. Or from making plans to work for as long as he could. He was fighting like mad with that broken sword — and his sheer unadulterated joy and good humor made everybody whose path he crossed fight harder with their good ones.

There was another boy at that college. His name was Merle and he had a whole sword and blessings to spare. He had music in him right down to his toes. We had a radio program together and he would sit at the organ without music and without any idea of what I was going to do. I didn't either, for we had no script, but we had a set of signals and I would signal him for bridges and he had a sixth sense for backgrounds and comments. He could make that organ sing and laugh and cry and wring the heart out of you with the sweetest music this side of heaven. After the program was over we would shriek with glee because it all came off well and we had ended, ad-libbing, at a proper spot.

Merle had a great future.

I met him a few years later at a place where I was about to do some stories. When I heard he was there I looked him up and asked him to play for me for old time's sake. While we were rehearsing I saw that his right arm was paralyzed and he had to pick up his hand and lift it to the keyboard. It was polio, he said simply, with no bid for pity. As he played he lifted that hand from the lower keyboard to the upper one and back again with such facility it was hard to realize that anything was wrong at all. But I knew he was settling for less in life than he'd originally hoped for, because every dream that boy had ever had was embodied in his music. His sword was not the keen one he'd started out with, but somewhere along the line, within his soul, he had made the decision to accept it as it was with quiet dignity and go on fighting.

There were others who crossed my path ever so briefly, but even a glimpse of them spurred me on to greater effort.

The young man whom polio doomed to a wheel chair for the rest of his life, and who could have rotted there, but he decided to write a book instead. I have an autographed copy of it; it's a brilliant book and for all I know he's already at work on another one.

And the man who is tops in the field of dubbing orchestral bridges and backgrounds into dramatic shows. It is an art that requires not only precision but great creative ability and a sixth sense for both music and drama. When we went to see him about the orchestration for a record album, we found him lying flat in a bed ingeniously rigged with an elaborate array of pulleys and gadgets — and completely surrounded with an unbelievable amount of equipment. He was brilliant, utterly charming and vitally alive — and almost totally paralyzed. The sword he'd picked up was a shattered one, but he was wielding it with skill as if it were whole.

And a woman I met ever so briefly who was left

not only paralyzed, but with no particular compensatory talents. By human standards there was absolutely no way she could stay in the battle at all. But stay she did. She brandished her sword in intercessory prayer, and the account of her victories, for all we know, may be one of the most glorious ones on the records in heaven.

And then there is my mother, who never for a moment thought of anything but staying in the battle. Whenever I've faltered in despondency and fear, I've thought of her and been too embarrassed to quit.

And then there was the woman who inspired the script in this chapter. When I met her she was a Sunday school teacher and—but if I tell any more now I'll spoil the story. She is Ellen in the script, and you can see for yourself what a fight she put up with her broken sword. The character of Millie is fictitious. "Unk" is the narrator.

* * * * *

THE BROKEN SWORD

I'll never forget the funny feeling that came over me when I went into the hospital room and saw Millie lying there. She looked so little in that high white hospital bed, and her hands and arms were all bandaged. I'd dreaded going — I hate hospitals anyhow — and I hated seeing Millie and facing her 'cause I knew what I was in for. I'd talked to young Tom, and I knew she was bitter. Awfully bitter.

I didn't really know Millie well enough to talk to her when she was bitter. I knew her only in the superficial way you know people when things are going well. Our firm had done her grandfather's accounting and then her father's. And though the old man was dead and I'd been retired for years, I'd formed the habit of dropping into the store occasionally to keep in touch.

I knew her as a little girl, wide-eyed and credulous, eager for stories. I saw her leap into the tomboy stage overnight. Some little girls miss it, unfolding like flowers, but Millie didn't. She met it head on and swaggered through it with aplomb that was both terrible and splendid. And then I saw her from afar as she retreated, shy and tremulous, as if to her, becoming a woman was a very private affair. Then she emerged laughing, half the old tomboy and the rest all secrets and mystery. And from then on, though she still called me "Unk," things were never the same with us. There were high school and boys. And then nurses' training. And boys. And then there was

Tom. I had just talked with him before I'd left for the hospital.

From the time I'd asked downstairs at the desk where her room was, and started for the elevators — I'd been trying to make up what I was going to say — but the elevators go up to her floor awfully quick — and before I knew it — a little half-pint-size nurse had whisked me down the hall without making a sound, and pushed open a door — and there I was. Alone with Millie. And feeling awkward.

Her face was turned away from me, and she didn't even bother to turn it toward me when she spoke.

"I don't want to see anyone. Go away."

"Now Millie — " I stood there turning my hat in my hand and feeling like a fool and wishing I knew what to say. I've never been much of a hand talking to folks. "I just want to be with you for a few minutes, Millie — let you know I'm standing by. I won't talk if you don't want me to."

"Oh it's you, Unk." She still didn't turn her head. "Thanks. Then you won't be saying the routine things. 'Keep your chin up it could be worse they're doing wonderful things with plastic surgery these days.' You can spare me that." It was a canned speech as though she'd had it ready. Then she said, "Tom sent you up, didn't he?"

137

"Yup. He did, Millie. But you know I would have come anyway."

"Yes — you would have. Unk — " She drew a deep breath and let it out and it came out all wavy as if the sobs were right behind it. "I love you. You've always been my friend ever since we moved here. But let's get this straight. I don't want to talk about me. My hands are burned. My arms are burned. They tell me I might not use them again — partial use at best. That's that and I don't want to talk any more about it. I won't marry Tom and I don't want to be drooled over and comforted and I don't want to hear about God and I won't make the best of it and I won't — "

"Wait a minute, Millie. You hadn't ought to get excited."

"I don't talk with my hands!" She shouted it. I waited for her to go on but she didn't. And then I tried a different tack.

"But Tom—" I started. And then I stopped. She'd turned her face to look at me and what I saw in her eyes stopped me short.

"Tom's being noble, wants to marry me anyhow. Isn't that wonderful?" she said. I wished she'd cry. But she didn't. Her voice got quiet instead. And deliberately reasonable. "Oh what's the use. We can't help talking about it, can we, Unk? There's nothing else to talk about. Go ahead, talk. You can't make it any worse. I'm — sorry I was so ugly. You just don't understand. You just don't *know* —"

"Maybe," I said. "Maybe not. But I do know Tom loves you, Millie. He wants to marry you because he *loves* you. Because he can't imagine life without you. And God loves you, too."

"No, not that. Don't give me that." She spoke to me as if I were a well-mannered, well-meaning child. "God doesn't love me. Look at me. Millie Barker, registered nurse. Owe no man anything and wouldn't harm a flea. But I run into a boiling cauldron and I'm burned to a crisp. I'd succumb to a real corny bromide and ask, 'Why does He allow these things to happen?' — but you'd try to answer and I know all the answers — they go around in circles."

"Speaking of the love of God," I said, "reminds me of a girl — for a minute you looked like her." I cleared my throat and plunged on. "She was a girl who dared. She had the soul of an adventurer." I didn't mean to say all that, but it was out.

"Oh, *no*," she moaned softly and turned her face back to the wall.

"Well, 'The Love of God' was her favorite hymn, that's all. That's why I mentioned it. 'The Love of God is greater far — than tongue or pen can ever tell. It reaches to the highest star—'" I knew I'd been dismissed. But somehow I couldn't go. "Well. Anyhow. This girl — her name was Ellen — had everything. Health — strength — beauty and brains, you might say. She was a young school teacher. That is, she was all set to be a school teacher. All set to be married, too. There were parties and — what d'you call 'em—"

"Showers?"

"Showers." I followed up my advantage quickly. "Yup. Clothes, plans, all the rest of it. And just before the wedding a few cases of polio broke out. She — she was one of them."

There was the clatter of dinner trays in the hall just then and it shattered the effect of what I'd said. It was like a sandbag dropping onto the stage just as you were about to disclose the first really important development in the play. I felt frustrated and foolish. I'd lost Millie's attention before I'd really gotten it. I muttered something like well, well, what was that, the dinner trays? And that I didn't know it was that late. And that I guessed I'd better be going.

"You're not going to finish the story?" she said, but without any real interest.

"Well, maybe it wasn't such a good idea to start it. I — I'll see you again, Millie."

She didn't answer, so I just backed out. Next thing I knew, I was in the elevator again, feeling like she hadn't really listened and I hadn't got anywhere.

But I'd underestimated the spell — yep, that's it — the spell a story can have over you.

Next day when I dropped in — I sat down, more at home this time, and Millie said—

"Well?"

"Well what?"

"Well — are you going on with the story? Did she get married?"

I paused and cleared my throat as if it were a new thought and I hadn't been thinking about it practically every minute since I'd seen her.

"Oh *that*. Well, not right away. The polio lasted a long time — months — and left her with one arm useless and the other with only partial use. But she got married."

"*Why?*" Millie said, and there was more incredulity behind it than if she'd made a speech.

"She knew John really loved her, wanted her. She dared. She dared face life as it was, asking no quarter. Took courage."

"I don't see how that took courage — being waited on — "

But I stopped her. "Hold on there. She didn't aim to be waited on. Any more than she could help it. John's first idea was to just take care of her, but she had other ideas — "

And I thought of Ellen and her other ideas.

141

"She was buzzing with determination all the while she was in the hospital and John was bringing pictures of the house they were building. But it wasn't until she was out of the hospital and on her feet that she took stock of her assets and the ideas began to take shape.

"It was spring when he first took her to the new house. It had the smell of new lumber and shavings and the air of excitement and promise that new houses have. They had walked into it from a warm spring rain outside. Ellen's hair was flat when she took her head scarf off and her face was rain-freshened and her eyes —

"'Ohhhh, John, it's a wonderful house,' she said, and she pushed her hair up with her good hand. 'A wonderful house.'

'And the kitchen,' John said. 'Watch out for the sawhorse. Here. Let me help you. How do you like it?' He liked to hear her say it again and again.

'It's wonderful,' she said. 'You can see for miles from these windows. I love it. And look — in the ravine. The violets are out.'

'They came out overnight. It's the warm rain.'

'I love the view from the kitchen.'

'It won't matter much, the kitchen. You won't be out here much.'

'What do you mean—won't be out here much.'

'Well, just to plan meals—'

'*Plan* meals? I'm going to *get* meals!'

'Ellen, let's get this straight. You're just going to — '

'I'm just going to stop living. Well, I won't. I can do — most things. I can't bend my arm or lift it but I can use my one hand.'

'Ellen—'

'So I can do things at arm's length. John — I've been thinking and thinking about it all. Look. If — if I could have a worktable built low — about like this — and things where I could reach them — there are so many things I can do. I can learn to do them *my* way! And don't look so alarmed!' She stopped, out of breath. She let out a loud grunt like an expletive, in mock exasperation and they both laughed. Then she said, 'John, try to understand. I want to live as if this — had just never happened. It isn't life as I wanted it. But it's life as it *is*. And that's the way I've got to live it. As it *is*.'

"She took a deep breath and said it matter-of-factly to cover the trembling in her voice. Ellen was all fight. He slipped his arm around her and she put her good arm around his waist and he took her paralyzed arm and drew it around his waist and held it there.

143

"They were married that spring.

"Ellen was all fight, all woman. She wasn't saintly or noble. John was glad. He watched her through the summer and then the winter months — her struggle in spite of the low counters, her wry and explosive exasperation with the incorrigible arm, her frustration in having a hand that would obey on the end of an arm that would not, that seemed not to be there. With Ellen, it sometimes even had a sense of the ridiculous. They found they could even laugh about it.

"Spring came suddenly the next year. It seemed to come overnight after a week of gentle warm rain. The blossoms were like dowagers at a flower show, fussing and chattering and pushing their way into the already crowded clusters.

"John's mother came to stay awhile and she was there when he brought Ellen home with the baby. He handed the child to his mother and helped Ellen through the house.

"She was ecstatic. 'John!' she said, You made me another low table. And all the baby's things where I can reach them!' They went into the living room. 'There's lots I can do for him. Almost everything.'

'Of course you can,' John's mother said quickly. 'We can share the work. Here, Ellen. Sit down. Put your feet on the rung of this chair. So. Now hold your bad hand with your good hand — make a cradle. Now you can hold your son. There.'

"Ellen sat down in the rocker carefully, getting the feel of her new slender body, and with a look of unconcealed triumph — like a child who has won out against great odds — cradled her son in her arms. 'Look, Son,' she whispered, in conspiracy. 'The violets are out. And I saw a robin this morning. We're going to have a terrific life together. I've got lots to show you and tell you. It's a *great* life — '

'Spring's out all over,' John said.

'I know,' she said. 'It just exploded. It isn't even *decent*!'

"It *was* a wonderful spring to usher a baby in. Flamboyant and extravagant and full of promises.

"In the next three years Ellen learned to cope with more and more things. She could jerk the offending arm into any position and she did so without self-consciousness. She treated it with polite respect but without pampering. She neither resented nor pitied it. It was just there to hang her hand on and she circumvented it — physically and emotionally.

"In the third year her body was heavy again and she could not kneel with her son to pray. She would sit on the edge of his bed, lowering herself carefully. And the child would pray.

"'Amen. Oh. And, Father, please help me get dressed in half the time tomorrow — ' she had given him the same matter-of-fact relationship that she had always had with God — 'and forgive me for taking twice the time today — but you know, Lord, that was an emergency on account of my suspenders. Amen.'

"She laughed softly. 'In Jesus' name, amen.'

'In Jesus name, amen. Why? Why do I *always* have to say that?'

'Because He died for you. And because you've accepted that gift of salvation. If you leave out Jesus you leave out the one who gives you the right to talk to God in the first place.'

'Oh.'

'You're right about wanting to dress quickly. You have to learn to do things for yourself now. You're going to help me take care of baby brother.'

'Oh, sure. I want to do that.' And then, 'I liked the story about Samson tonight. He was a strong guy, all right.'

'Yes — holding her arm. 'He had a strong body and great gifts. But he was a failure. He missed the best God had for him.'

'What's tomorrow's story?'

'Tomorrow I'll tell you about a woman who hid two enemy spies and cast her lot with God — '

"And so it would go. She would kiss him goodnight at last. They had good times together.

"Spring was late that year. The cold rains kept beating it back. And then there was an April snow. So when Ellen came home with her second son only the crocuses were up, poking through. The other blossoms were held back tight and shivering. And the violets were hidden down in the ravine, waiting. So when spring finally came it was cautious and wary and then, belated and flustered, it scurried through the briefest possible token gestures and hurried into summer almost overnight.

"The years went by and the springs came inexorably; it was only how they came that was unpredictable. Sometimes in perfect order. And sometimes like a first-night performance, after many false starts and muffled groans and abortive curtain-risings.

"And the offending arm because less and less an issue. It had nothing to do with their love, Ellen's and John's.

" 'I've been asked to teach Sunday school,' she told John one night. They were standing in the kitchen. She was holding a stack of towels in her good arm.

'I know better than to ask if you said yes.'

'Sure I said yes. The boys are in school. I have hours to myself. Will you scratch my nose?'

" He did.

" 'It's a women's class,' she said. 'I've a list here somewhere. I can pray for each one of them. It'll be a good class, John. It'll make me dig.'

'Uh huh.'

'I need to dig.'

'Yes.'

'And, John?'

'Yes?'

'It's a wonderful life.'

"He took the towels, put them on the counter.

'I love you,' he said.

'I love *you*. I'm so glad I talked you into marrying me.' There was laughter in her voice. But lots of years went into the way she said it."

I thought of Ellen and the way she said "I love you." I stopped talking, thinking about it.

"You made it sound wonderful," said Millie. Her voice startled me.

"Yes — it *was* a wonderful life," I said. "All the way through. She made it wonderful. Right up until she left it. The letters she wrote the boys while they were at school — ah — nobody else ever wrote such letters. The class she taught, the lives she touched — somehow, with her, even death wasn't horrible. You knew she had just crossed over."

"She died?"

"People like Ellen never really die, Millie. She just — crossed over, like Christian did in *Pilgrim's Progress* — she was always talking to the boys about Christian. She crossed over and saw the one who had given her that burden — and knew at last why He'd given it. And there, she had two strong arms at last. But she'd done pretty well without 'em. I think He said, 'Well done, thou good and faithful servant.'"

"Yeah —"

"Her life reached out and blessed everybody it touched, everywhere — her influence made something special out of ordinary things."

"You must have known her pretty well."

"Yes — I knew her very well." And then I told Millie what I was sure she had guessed all along. "You see — I was John."

But incredibly she hadn't guessed. Whether in the colossal egotism of youth she couldn't imagine that an old man like myself could have loved a woman I don't know. But she hadn't guessed.

"Oh. And I thought you didn't understand," she said and all her defenses crumpled as she said it and her face got very vulnerable, like a little girl's. "Unk, I've known you so long. But I've never really known you." Then desperately, "Her life did count, didn't it? It *did* count?"

"There are many who think so. Some she taught in Sunday school have gone on to Christian work. Her two sons grew up in the knowledge of God — one is a Christian businessman — the other is a preacher. And their sons — my grandsons — one's a missionary and the other one is being ordained next month. I'm going to the ordination. Gonna sit right in the front row. He promised to wink at me."

"Ohhhh, *Unk*."

"You see, Millie — the life she dared to live is still going on. Do you think it was worth living? Do you think it counted?"

She sniffed unashamedly. "That hymn — *her* hymn. What was it, Unk?"

"I never finished it, did I? 'The love of God — is greater far — than tongue or pen — can ever tell — it reaches to the highest star —' It reaches to the lowest hell, Millie. It was as if she had a broken sword to fight the battle with. Not a nice new shiny one. But she aimed to fight anyway. With the broken one."

I got a tissue from her table and wiped her nose while I was talking. She let me do it, not taking her eyes off me.

"I don't know why God gave her a broken

sword," I said. "I don't aim to try to explain those things. I only know that God's love was there — in her life — just shining all through."

She crumpled then all over and turned her face away and began to cry softly to herself. There's all kinds of crying and ordinarily I would have worried but I saw that this was good. And then I saw that young Tom had slipped into the room and was standing there behind me. I turned and we just nodded in a kind of unspoken conspiracy. And then I left.

Going down the elevator I felt Ellen's presence so strongly I reached up and patted my shoulder where her hand seemed to be resting.

All the sadness came suddenly with the cold rain outside. Spring would be late this year. I felt empty. But as I rounded the corner by the parking lot I stopped in a sudden gust of wind, my head down. And there they were, huddled in some leaves shivering. Violets. I stooped and picked a couple. In the car I put them in my buttonhole.

I started the car and turned on the windshield wipers. They swept clean arcs and through the arcs I saw the world washed and the buds waiting and some of the sadness left me. Spring would be late, but it would come.

Like I said, I'm not much good at talking to people. And I don't know if I really got to Millie. Or if she'll marry young Tom.

But if she does — why there's another life that Ellen has reached out and touched.

I thought as I drove out of the parking lot — there just doesn't seem to be any end to it.

* * * * *

Now I must get academic for a moment and confess that I've tampered with facts a bit, but only for dramatic value. I made "Unk" an old man, for instance, because that way it was more feasible that Millie would not know about his distant past. It also lessened the possibility that the listener would guess who he was until the proper time to disclose it. He was given the unidentifiable name of "Unk" for the same reason.

John's real name is not John at all, but Carl— and Ellen's real name is Luella, and the happiest confession I have to make is that she is really still alive and still teaching Sunday school in upper New York State.

As you've probably guessed, she was *my* Sunday school teacher, and the first one I had, as an adult. I'd stayed away from Sunday school for years, but now Gary was old enough to go and Steve seemed content in a basket in the corner so

I decided to give it a try.

I first noticed with what dexterity she manipulated her notes and her Bible with only one good hand and a paralyzed arm. The other arm and hand were completely useless. Then I noticed her eyes. They were brown, and "sparkling eyes" is an expression so overworked it has lost its meaning, but when Luella looked at you with hers, there were no other words for them. They had one sparkle for enthusiasm and one for warmth and a special gentle one for tenderness. And I never saw her when she didn't have one of them turned on. Then I noticed her smile. Ah, that was a good one, that smile. It was one to make you glad you were alive.

But perhaps the most revealing thing I can say about her is that after a while I didn't notice Luella any more as she taught. I saw only God.

They are still living there in Burnt Hills — "Ellen" and "John"—and their farm is a show place that has been photographed and written about—and it does your heart good to be with them and see the wonderfully full life they've both worked out—with a broken sword.

The world is full of people with broken swords. Some of them have, like the soldier in the fable, fled to the edge of the battle where they could hide. And there are some who have thought they were *going* to have broken swords and bore it nobly, but the sword did not break after all. And they've had a sneaking feeling of pride ever since about how well they behaved and how completely they gave it to God — when perhaps the only reason God did not go ahead and break the sword was because He could not trust them with such a responsibility, for they were not really up to it after all.

The nearest I ever came to a broken sword was after a spinal fusion when for several days there was a question as to whether the partially atrophied muscles in one of my legs would be restored. A steel brace perhaps, or crutches. Or at best, a limp. I lay in the hospital thinking about it — numb. Too terrified even to rebel. Then I began methodically to die again to everything I could possibly think of that meant anything to me — to give it all to God. For a while I found I could give Him everything but that. Well, all right, I would settle for a limp. And then one night as I was going down the list for the hundredth time I suddenly laughed aloud at the absurdity of my struggle. If I was completely in His hands — then I *was* — steel brace, limp and all! I gave to to Him — and slept like a baby.

Well, it turned out that in a week or so I could wiggle my toes. In a year I couldn't have told you which leg had been the culprit. So I can't feel noble about it because I never really had the broken sword. I never really chafed under the steel brace or suffered the crutches or even limped. Anyone can give himself in a sudden moment of abandonment. But who is to say I would not have wavered and finally fled in panic, after I'd settled down to the reality of it?

The ones who have decided to stay in the battle had to stop brooding about what they didn't have and concentrate on what they *did* have — and sharpen it and polish it until it was a weapon to reckon with. Some of them discovered potentialities they never knew were there when they were busy bustling about. And all of them realized a great truth, whether or not they put it into words. They knew that though they were limited physically — some of them forced into complete physical idleness — the part of them that *counted* was still intact.

It is the idleness of the *mind* that leaves us floating like aimless debris, getting nowhere. It is the idleness of the *soul* that makes us deadweight. For it is when we are mentally and spiritually idle that we pick up the attitudes and habits that set us drifting and in the end drag us down: The sloths of despondency, clinging to the dark branches of our minds. The minor chords of complaining, reverberating down endless corridors in dull monotony. The chisel of criticism, chipping off the good and leaving ragged edges. The dreary treadmills of destructive habits, refusing to let us off. And anger. And hate. And bitterness . . .

These things are there, in all of us, all the time, clamoring for attention. And it is when we are mentally and spiritually idle that they get it.

In *The Holy War*, it was when the inhabitants of Mansoul began to court Mr. *Carnal-Security* and forgot to go to the palace for the feasts that Prince Emmanuel had spread for them, that these "Diabolonians" came out of hiding. They'd been sweating it out in cracks and cellars for years, awaiting their opportunity. They sneaked out into the side streets, a bit cautiously at first, but no one paid them any heed, and so they began to stay out openly in the market square. It was while Mansoul was *spiritually idle* that they struck. It's the part that *counts* that we must keep intact. "My grace is sufficient for thee: for my strength is made perfect in weakness" is as true today as when He first said it.

God did not intend that anyone flee in panic to the side of the battle and hide. And some of the swords that have won the most glorious victories — have been the broken ones. It is the ones who are fighting with broken swords who spur the rest of us on. . . .

CHAPTER 7

DEATH IS A PRIVATE AFFAIR

*Except a corn of wheat fall into the ground
and die, it abideth alone: but if it die,
it bringeth forth much fruit.*

He that loveth his life shall lose it . . .

He gives by halves who hesitates to give.
        . . . Broome, Letter to Lord Cornwallis

Then there is an old fable about a beggar who sat every day by the roadside with his bowl and begged the passers-by to give him some rice. One day, as the story goes, he was sitting there when a prince came along. The prince ordered his carriage to stop, and he leaned out and what he said gave the beggar the surprise of his life. He asked the poor chap to give *him* what was in the bowl. Now apparently it had been a bad day for the beggar, and he had collected only half a bowl of rice. Having a strong sense of self-preservation, he naturally demurred. To give this prince, who already had everything, his half-bowl of rice seemed the height of folly. But after a long and searching look from the prince, the beggar was disarmed and in a state of complete abandonment he held up his bowl. Whereupon the prince calmly took everything in it and drove on . . .

We'll get to the rest of the story after a bit, for if you have read it you know there is more and if you have not you know this is no way for a fable to end. No beggar ever got left dangling without a denouement in any fable worth its salt. And this beggar was no exception — but at this point it does seem as if he went overboard on the business of giving and his prospects look grim.

To be asked to share is easy, for we take that as a matter of course and as a part of living. To be asked to give up something is not too difficult, for most of us are pretty generous. To be asked to give up much *is* a bit more difficult, however, for not many of us are noble. When it comes to giving up everything, a chosen few would rise to the occasion. But to be asked to give up everything, when "everything" means not only all that we have but all we do and plan to do and all that we *are* — staggers the imagination. Even when it is God who is doing the asking, it gives us quite a jolt. Wasn't conversion enough?

At first we cannot believe that He asked that. And then we find that He did. "If any man will come after me, let him *deny himself*, and take up his cross, and follow me" (Matt. 16:24).

Then we tell ourselves He couldn't really have meant it. And then we find that He did. "Whosoever . . . forsaketh not all that he hath, *he cannot be my disciple*" (Luke 14:33).

And now we find ourselves in the position of the poor beggar, who probably looked behind him, hoping the prince was speaking to somebody else and not making this outrageous demand of *him*. We tell ourselves Christ must have meant it just for the disciples and spiritual giants. We'll concede that He said it and even that He meant it — as long as He didn't mean *us*. But He did. "What? know ye not that . . . *ye* are not your own? For *ye* are bought with a price: therefore glorify God in your body, and in your spirit, which are God's" (I Cor. 6:19,20).

So there is the whole offensive truth. For these

are and always have been hard words, and many who heard them from Christ Himself turned away. It is still offensive to many of us today. But whether or not we accept it, it is still there, none the less, in black and white — written into the covenant Christ made with those who belong to Him. It is like the "small print" portion of a contract. We might stumble over it, find it a bother, or choose to ignore it — but we cannot do away with it. We are bound by the whole contract and all its terms, and if it is true that we have a right to its benefits it is equally true that we are committed to its demands.

And Christ unequivocally demands all of us.

If we have accepted the contract thus far, it is at this point that we begin to dicker. And it is at this point that our powers of specious reasoning reach such lofty heights that if it were not a time-wasting, strength-sapping tragedy, it would be ludicrous. There is no end to the pets and privileges we want to hang onto, and no end to the ingenious ways we can devise to make the culprits look legitimate. Bunyan knew this and exposed it with deadly accuracy in the dialogue between Prince Emmanuel and Diabolus' emissary, in *The Holy War*. Emmanuel had besieged the town of Mansoul, and Diabolus knew his defeat was imminent. But he was determined to salvage as much as he could, and sent out to Emmanuel's camp a chap who was thoroughly schooled in the art of dickering. This gentleman got right to the point. "In order that all may know how great a lord my master is," he said, drawing off his gloves, "he is willing to let you have half of Mansoul — either half you say."

"Mansoul is mine," said Emmanuel. "I will not give up half."

"Very well." The emissary gave in quickly. "Have it your way. Then he is willing to let you have *all* of Mansoul — with this proviso. That he be allowed to keep just one little part — any part you say."

"I will not give up one little part. I bought Mansoul with my blood. The answer is no."

"You are a hard man, sire," the emissary sighed. "Suppose — suppose my master Diabolus leaves Mansoul *all* to you — provided some of his relatives stay there and maintain their businesses. They won't bother anyone. Surely you cannot object to that."

"I do object to that."

"Ah," sighed the emissary with gentle patience. "You are being difficult. Very well then. My master *and* his relatives will move out. Provided he will be allowed to come back and visit on occasion."

"No. Mansoul is mine, twice mine. Mine by gift from my Father and mine by purchase. I cannot allow it."

"Just *visit*? A few days at a time? He wouldn't stay long."

"No."

"May he send them gifts then — just an occasional token of his esteem and friendship? For old times' sake?"

"No."

"Letters perhaps?"

"No."

"Notes?"

"No."

The emissary drew on his gloves reluctantly and sighed again. "Well just suppose," he said innocently, "that someone in Mansoul had business that had to be done — shall we say in a certain way? And nobody but my master could help him? Could he meet him outside the city walls just long enough to transact the — "

"They shall have no business that my Father cannot handle. By prayer and supplication with thanksgiving they will let their requests be made known to Him."

The emissary walked slowly to the door and sighed again. "Very well," he said. "I shall tell my master your answers — eh — answer."

He had tried every loophole, every possibility. But there was only one answer. Prince Emmanuel unequivocally demanded all of Mansoul. Christ unequivocally demands all of us.

With the terms of the contract explained and the dickering dispensed with, there is only one thing left to do. It amounts to unconditional surrender. And unconditional surrender means death to the power of the capitulating army.

"Therefore we are buried with him by baptism into death . . . " (Rom. 6:4).

"Except a corn of wheat fall into the ground and die . . . " (John 12:24).

"Now if we be dead with Christ . . . " (Rom. 6:8).

"Reckon ye also yourselves to be dead indeed unto sin . . . " (Rom. 6:11).

"For ye are dead . . . " (Col. 3:3).

This was not an admonition for the prophets and apostles alone. It was for the great parade of Christians marching, "terrible as an army with banners," down through the ages.

It is for the spiritual giants.

George Müller said in a letter published in *The Christian* (British): "For the first four years after I became a believer in the Lord Jesus, it was for a good part in great weakness; but then it came with me to an entire and full surrender of heart. I gave myself fully to the Lord. Honors, pleasure, money, my physical powers, my mental powers, all were laid down at the feet of Jesus." He summed it up in one pithy sentence: "One day George Müller died."

Frances Ridley Havergal wrote: "I had hoped that a kind of table-land had been reached in my journey, where I might walk a while in the light, without the weary succession of rock and hollow, crag and morass, stumbling and striving; but I seem borne back into all the old difficulties of the way. I think that the great root of all my trouble and alienation is that I do not now make an unconditional surrender of myself to God; and until this is done I shall know no peace. I am sure of it." Well, Frances did just that. And it had a very practical effect on her life. She vouched for it years later when she said: "I've seen the light. And what you see you can never *unsee*. There must be full surrender before there can be full blessedness. God admits you by the one into the other." Frances is the writer of the hymn — "Take My Life . . . "

David Brainerd said in his journal in 1743: "I felt exceedingly dead to the world and all its enjoyments; I was ready to give up life, and all its comforts, as soon as called to it; and yet then had as much comfort of life as almost ever I had. Life itself appeared but an empty bubble; the riches, honors, and enjoyments of it extremely tasteless. I longed to be entirely *crucified* to all things here below. My soul was sweetly resigned to God's disposal of me; and I saw there had nothing happened to me but what was best for me . . . it was my meat and drink to be holy, to live to the Lord, and to die to the Lord."

Dwight L. Moody responded to the challenge, "The world has yet to see what God can do through one man completely yielded to Him," by crying out: "Let *me* be that man!"

And it is for ordinary people.

Many years ago I knew a very ordinary girl who decided not to sleep or eat until she had settled the matter. That night she wrote out a statement declaring her own death, not unlike a death certificate, and listed all the things she thought she ought to die to. The most obvious things came first. She died to her pride, her ambition, her rights and desires, and all the rest of it. Then, of course, her faults. She was generous to a fault, trusting to a fault, too honest, too meek, and perhaps a wee bit quick to get righteously indignant when tried beyond the bounds of reason. Then came other faults which she preferred to call weaknesses. By 2 A.M. some of the real faults came to light, and by 3 A.M. the faults and attitudes and desires that were shocking to write down. Then came her assets, and that was more difficult than ever for it is when we die to our so-called "good points" that we really squirm. From 4 to 5 A.M. she walked the floor, asking God to show her more and more things to add to the list until at last it was as complete as she could get it, and then she gave Him carte blanche with regard to any omissions she may have made. Now all this was done with a great deal of soul searching, for the girl was desperately in earnest and did not want to sign it until, and indeed unless, she meant it. At last at 6 A.M. she did sign it, and it was a silent and solemn — and secret — moment.

A bit dramatic? Perhaps. But this girl couldn't do anything without making a production out of it, and she did the thing in a way that was most meaningful to her. You die your way. She died hers.

There is no format, any more than there is a prescribed way to react to conversion. One person may walk down the aisle and accept Christ as the divine Son of God and as his Saviour with tears and demonstration. Another may make the same commitment quietly in the pew, in his car, or in the middle of an alfalfa field. But both have "believed on the Son of God" and stepped from condemnation into eternal life. Each has made this very personal transaction in his own way.

And so it is with complete capitulation to Christ. It is described as both full surrender and death to self, and the meanings are interchangeable. Some of us make the transaction at the time we are converted. Some of us stumble upon it later by one means or another. Some of us miss it entirely. And some of us choose to ignore it. Actually it is as much an ultimatum to the Christian as the terms of conversion are to the sinner. And it is not for the spiritual giants alone. It should be the norm.

And so we completely surrender ourselves and thereby die to our own plans, our own life, our own ambitions. What a dismal thought!

"What?" screamed old Mr. Unbelief to the gentry of Mansoul, in *The Holy War.* "Would you take the staff out of your own hands and give it to One with unlimited power? Do you realize you will no longer be your own?" He was so horrified at this prospect that he frothed at the mouth. That was when old Diabolus stepped in and suggested that some dickering might be in order. Surely such complete capitulation would be sheer insanity! A few provisos would light it up a bit.

But both Unbelief and Diabolus were carefully refraining from telling the gentry of Mansoul the whole story. They were withholding valuable information that would "comfort and benefit the opponent." It was their strategy to disclose only the first part and leave the picture a grim one. Indeed, if we stopped here, it *would* be a dreary business. But let's get back for a moment to the poor beggar in our fable and see how he made out.

He looked at the prince's carriage as it went on down the road, and his feelings were a queer mixture of elation, abandonment and wonder, for he had just done something beyond all reason. And then he sighed and then he sobered and got back to the business at hand. He began to cry out to passers-by and beg for rice and hold up his empty bowl — but wait a minute. It wasn't empty. He looked in it, incredulous. For every grain of rice the prince had taken, he had left a ruby . . .

And that is what changes the picture.

For if it is true that "Therefore we are buried with him by baptism into death . . . ," the rest of the verse is equally true: "that like as Christ was raised up from the dead by the glory of the Father, even so we also should walk in *newness of life*." If it is true that "Except a corn of wheat fall into the ground and die, it abideth alone . . . ," it is also true that "if it die it *bringeth forth much fruit*." If it is true that "Now if we be dead with Christ . . . ," it is also true that "we believe that we shall also *live with him*." If it is true that you should "Reckon ye also yourselves to be dead indeed unto sin . . . ," the rest is true: *"but alive unto God through Jesus Christ our Lord.* And if this is true: "For ye are dead . . . ," then so is this: *"and your life is hid with Christ in God."* Christ came that we "might have life, and . . . have it *more abundantly*."

George Müller established the famous orphanages at Bristol. His life is a legend. Frances Ridley Havergal's name is a household word. Countless thousands have been blessed by her hymns and devotional works. David Brainerd's work among the American Indians has made him immortal. He had a hard life, it is true, but here's what he thought about it: "I enjoyed such a heaven, as far exceeded the most sublime conceptions of an unregenerate soul; and even unspeakably beyond what I myself could conceive at another time." Dwight Moody's life was happier beyond anything *he* could have conceived. And the girl who signed her death certificate was capitulated into an undreamed-of ministry. Not one of them would have swapped what God gave them in return, for all the gold in the world.

Each one surrendered in his own way, according to his understanding of the matter, up to the light he had, and consistent with his own personality. Just as the capitulation is an individual matter — so are the rewards. God deals with us personally, as individuals, and he doesn't give any two of us exactly the same thing. Everybody's "bowl of rubies" means something different. In *The Holy War*, when the inhabitants of Mansoul went to Prince Emmanuel's love feasts at the palace, he discoursed with them on many subjects and before they left, gave each of them "secret gifts" and no two were the same. The kind of life He gives one will not be the kind of life He chooses to give another. It is not that He gives you the life you want, but that if you have "put on the mind of Christ," you want the life He gives you. And to take liberty with an old axiom: "One man's bowl of rubies is another man's poison." The life He chooses for one person might be unthinkable to another.

The life He chose for the woman in the following story was unthinkable to her family and to her friends. It even seemed so to her, at first. But He kept speaking to her about it, and when she had at last given up herself and surrendered to Him without reservation — she found it *was* the life she wanted. And from that moment, she could dream of doing nothing else.

Her name was Mathilde Wrede.

Her "bowl of rubies" was the presence of Christ, and having tasted this, she could settle for nothing less. The best things life had to offer could not stand up against it. And here is her story.

* * * * *

HE WHO LOSES HIS LIFE . . .

"He who finds his life shall lose it, and he who loses his life for my sake shall find it."

This is a story of a girl who lost her life — just threw it away — and she had a fabulous life to throw away, too. She was the daughter of the provincial governor of Vasa, Finland. The best things life could offer were hers — wealth — good family — education. . . . And the best things life could promise were hers to come — a good marriage — a brilliant social life — children. . . . But this made-to-order life took an unexpected twist and got mixed up with, of all people, prisoners. It was a most unlikely twist for a girl like Mathilde, and here is how it happened.

Mathilde was used to prisoners. She grew up in the midst of them — they were always on the grounds of her father's huge estate making repairs, tending the beautiful gardens. They were always watched by guards — they seldom spoke — they looked despondent or sulky or mean — or desperate. Being a little girl, she didn't think of them as *people* even — until one day when she was with her father on some business at the prison. She got tired of waiting and listening to grown-up talk, and wandered off, unnoticed. She opened doors and peeked in rooms — it was all great fun until she opened one door — and stood there, horrified. The smith was welding red hot irons on the ankles of some prisoners — they screamed in rage and pain as the guards held them down. . . .

Mathilde closed the door quickly — and hurried back to the offices where her father was. A matron was frantically looking for her.

"Mathilde! Where have you been?"

"I — just down the corridor."

"Your father will be furious if he finds I have let you wander. He is about ready to leave. My child — you look so white — what is the matter?"

"Nothing. I — I want to go home."

Mathilde was quiet on the way home, and all through dinner. And that night when her nurse put her to bed —

"And now we must tuck you in. Your French tutor comes first thing in the morning. You must have a good night's sleep so you will be fresh and bright. And then your music and then your dancing."

"Ingrid — "

"Yes, dear."

"This furniture — in my bedroom — and my sitting room. It was made by prisoners, wasn't it?"

"But of course. Your father had it made especially for you for your birthday. It is exquisite. Any little girl would be proud to own such — "

"Made by prisoners. I — I don't like it anymore. I used to think it was pretty, but now I don't like it."

"My child, you're crying. What *is* wrong?"

"Ingrid — " Mathilde's voice sank to a whisper. "They were burning the iron bands right on their skin. Right on their *skin*. I saw them. I peeked in the room and saw them. They screamed and screamed — " She burst into weeping. "I closed the door and ran and ran and ran but I could still hear them screaming."

And after that, prisoners were people —

desperate, hopeless people. Mathilde's heart began to be conditioned for her life's work.

The years that followed were filled with music and languages and culture befitting a governor's daughter, and adding up to a life that would be of considerable account, as this world judges lives.

And then her sense of values got picked up by God and turned upside down, and nothing was ever quite the same again.

She went to a revival meeting. It was as simple as that. And she heard the golden words: "For God so loved the world, that he gave his only begotten Son, that whosoever believeth in him should not perish, but have everlasting life."

Mathilde Wrede — beautiful, talented and wealthy, who needed nothing from anyone — knelt before a holy God and confessed her need of Christ as her Saviour. She had never heard the verses:

"That if thou shalt confess with thy mouth the Lord Jesus, and shalt believe in thine heart that God hath raised him from the dead, thou shalt be saved.

"For with the heart man believeth unto righteousness; *and with the mouth confession is made unto salvation.*"

But she did not need to. It was in her heart, and she could not keep it to herself.

She told her father first —

"Father — father!"

"Yes, Mathilde?"

"I'm saved."

"Do you feel all right?"

"Oh, I'm quite all right. Do you know the Lord Jesus died for you?"

"Yes, I expect He died for the whole world. I've never thought too much about it."

"I never did either until last night — 'gave his only begotten Son' suddenly came alive for me; 'that whosoever believeth on him' suddenly *meant* something. I realized that I never really *believed* until I was overwhelmed by it, brought to my knees by it. Then I believed and something happened to me."

"Mathilde, you're weeping." His voice was soft.

"I know. I want to *do* something. *Tell* someone. Tell *everybody*."

"My child. You act like one in love."

"I *am* in love. It is a love greater than one human being can have for another. I — I want to tell everyone."

And she did. It was too wonderful to keep to herself.

And then one day she struck up a conversation with a prisoner who worked on the grounds —

"Hello."

"Good afternoon, Miss."

"Do you mind if I talk to you while you repair that door?"

"No, Miss. I don't mind."

"How long have you been a prisoner?"

"Fourteen years, it's been."

"Oh, I was a prisoner all my life, until a few weeks ago. Then I was pardoned."

"Do you feel all right, Miss?"

"Oh, quite. What were you condemned for?"

He stared at her for a minute. "For theft, Miss."

"I was condemned for unbelief. But someone paid the penalty for me. I had a pardon waiting for me and didn't even know it until a few weeks ago."

He straightened up slowly and looked at her in amazement. She laughed softly. "I wanted to make you curious."

The guard started toward them.

"It's all right," Mathilde said, "I want to talk to this gentleman. He's not bothering me." She turned back to the prisoner and spoke softly again, as if they were in conspiracy. "You are condemned to much more than prison. You are condemned to eternal separation from the God who made you. And the charge is worse than theft — the charge is unbelief. He who believeth, his sins are forgiven him and he hath eternal life. It says that in the Bible.

There is pardon and forgiveness waiting for you if you will only take it."

He stared at her, incredulous. Both at what she was saying and that she, the governor's daughter, was saying it.

"There is another kind of hope and freedom," she went on quickly. "Born into the glorious freedom of being the sons of God." And then, "You weep, my friend."

"Yes, Miss. You should" — But then he stopped. She was the governor's daughter.

"I should what?"

"You should — I wish you could come out and tell us prisoners about it." He turned back to his task, embarrassed by his boldness. But Mathilde looked at him in new excitement.

"Why — why — I *shall!*" she cried. "I think I can get permission. Yes — I think I shall!"

And incredibly she did get permission. There were visits to the prison frequently after that — whenever they could be squeezed into her busy social life.

At first they were something to do — new and a bit frightening. And then they were a part of her, both draining and nourishing her. And then God brought her to the place where she would hold her life, as if it were a tangible thing, in her two hands and decide whether or not to throw it away. . . .

When it started, it didn't seem important. Not that important. She was in her sitting room with Ingrid.

"Ingrid, you will ruin your eyes in this light. Here. That's better. Oh — my lovely white gown."

"I am making an alteration. It is for tomorrow night."

"Tomorrow night? Oh *no*."

"Have you forgotten you promised to accompany your father and some friends to the concert?"

"Ohhhh. I promised to go to the prison."

Ingrid sighed. "But this is more important, my dear. You cannot be running to the prison all the time. You are young. You owe something to yourself."

"Ohhh. And father will be hurt." She considered that. "All right—I'll go with father. I'll postpone my prison visit until later in the week."

It seemed simple enough. There were other times to visit the prisoners. Her father did need her. And she was young. She went to bed and to sleep.

But she slept fitfully. Uneasiness plagued her, and a vague feeling of guilt—and cries of prisoners, felt rather than heard, and then—

She sat up suddenly.

There was a *prisoner* in her room — chains hanging from his hands and feet. He walked toward her — and stood looking at her with sorrowful eyes.

"What are you doing here?" she whispered. She did not know whether she was awake or asleep. But he spoke!

"Thousands of poor chained prisoners sigh for life, freedom — peace. Speak to them the Word of Him who can make them free, so long as you have time."

"Who — who *are* you?" she whispered. But he was already gone. It seemed so real, so real. But of course it was a dream. She stared into the darkness of her room beyond the moonlight. As long as I have time, she thought. And she knew it was no dream.

"Thou shalt go to all that I shall send thee, and whatsoever I command thee thou shalt speak." She could see no one in the room now, but she heard it clearly. As long as I have time, she thought.

"Get thee to them of the captivity and speak to them." She heard it again.

"Oh, God, God" — she spoke aloud this time. "I am not strong. I am so young — "

"He who loses his life for my sake shall find it."

It was quiet, so quiet.

"Then I give thee my life." She heard her

own voice say it clearly, in the dark. Then she came suddenly alive, more alive than she'd ever been in her life before. "My life is thine." This time she cried it exultantly. And all the fear was gone and all the weakness and there was nothing left but love, too great to bear, too great to bear. . . .

And so she threw her life away. For forty years, Mlle. Wrede, the Baroness Wrede, ministered to men and women behind prison bars. She ministered, and there streamed through her a strength and a depth and a hot sympathy for those prisoners, and a heart on fire for the Lord Jesus Christ.

She wasn't a "lady" slumming; she lived on the same fare as the prisoners and they knew it. Her ministry blazed down through the terrors that the Russian revolution had spilled over into Finland. She dealt with the worst of men and women, pointing them the way to the Saviour — she became a very part of their sufferings.

Many years later at Wiborg, where groups of prisoners were being dispatched to the Siberian mines for life — a slight figure made its way down a dark prison corridor and was let into a cell. It was Mlle. Wrede.

"Ah, my friend," she said, "You sent for me."

"Yes, Mlle. Wrede. I have something for you. I have been carving it for many weeks."

"A brooch! Carved from ivory. It is exquisite, beautiful! But, my friend, where on *earth* did you get hold of ivory?"

"It is not ivory. I carved it from an old soup bone. It has been in the sunshine for a long time to dry out the particles of grease."

She examined it, incredulous. "You made this lovely jewel — from an old soup bone! Impossible!"

"But you have said that God can deliver a man as bad as I have been. The sun of His love can consume all my sins, as the power of sunshine has cleansed this bone."

"God bless you, my friend. You are — "

But the cries outside in the courtyard told them there was another batch of prisoners leaving for Siberia.

"I must go," she said quickly. "I shall see you again, my friend. And, oh, thank you!" She touched his hand and was gone.

As she crossed the courtyard, an arm stretched out through every grated window to her. And someone called out from the line of prisoners: "Farewell, thou dearest daughter of our Fatherland, thou true friend of the prisoners — " She stood, her arms outstretched, her face lifted: "Farewell, my dear friends. Look up! I shall see you again — when He comes!" And she said softly to herself: "Lord Jesus, come quickly!"

She stood in the courtyard until they were out of sight, and then went back into the prison — the woman who, by all worldly standards, had thrown her life away.

Her last words, though, before she died a few years later didn't sound at all like the words of a woman who had lost all.

She said, "Tonight I cross the frontier. Can anyone be as happy as I!"

He who loses his life for my sake shall find it.

* * * * *

Now a story like this is discouraging indeed. If a frail little woman like Mathilde could dash off, lead a life of derring-do, and surmount seemingly insurmountable odds, what on earth are the rest of us doing? It is a problem that bears some discussion, for this is another point where we go amiss. After understanding the contract and accepting its terms thus far, it is a tragic thing to stumble here and spoil it all.

First, we have such a penchant for being influenced that even after being convinced in our souls that we are where God wants us to be, one whiff of another's life is enough to make us sniff and prick up our ears — and wonder if we'd got the thing quite straight after all. A missionary's fiery testimony that he was never really surrendered until he became a missionary leaves us a bit unsettled, for the implication is that if he is surrendered, then we, sitting there comfortable in the pews, cannot be. If we are, we wonder guiltily, how dare we be so comfortable.

Some of the most misleading exponents of surrender are those who would lead us to believe that the only way to "die" and be successful about it is to go into full-time Christian service. God does not say that. It is true that Moses dropped his sheepherding business and devoted the rest of his life to leading the Israelites from Egypt to Canaan. Noah dropped what he was doing and made building the ark and preaching righteousness his obsession.

But Christ let Zacchaeus go right back into business — only this time as an honest man.

He did not urge men into full-time service but sent them back into the world to live ordinary lives. And the touchstone of their surrender was that they were, whatever they were doing, completely *His*. To be completely His is to be in full-time service in any kind of life — "instant in season, out of season" — being "ready always to give . . . a reason of the hope that is in you."

Then there are other ways in which we can stumble at this point. For we also have a penchant for doubting that plagues us to the end, and a few unexpected turns in our course can catapult us into a limbo of uncertainty and make us wonder if we didn't perhaps make a mistake after all. Bunyan himself confessed that in the depth of his soul, the monsters Doubt and Unbelief periodically stirred and clamored for attention. Perhaps that is why old Mr. Unbelief was one of the arch-villains in *The Holy War*. After Mansoul's first great victory, old Diabolus' coup was his use of Unbelief and his army of doubters, and when they had at last been crushed by Captain Faith's army, he still managed to smuggle more of them in through his espionage campaign. And even John the Baptist, when he was in prison, sent messengers to Jesus asking Him if He were really the Christ after all, or should they look for another!

And alas, we are also such incurable busybodies that even if we are settled and sure of it, we have a penchant for openly or secretly wondering what God is doing about the other fellow and if that fellow is really in his right place. And if he is allowing himself something we have given up, how can he really be surrendered anyhow? We check him against our own list of "dos and don'ts," paste him up on a sort of spiritual graph, and sigh if it doesn't measure up. If he *is* measuring up we still cannot resist analyzing and wondering about his life or his ministry or his problems; our curiosity is insatiable. God's admonition concerning this particular "talent" of ours is that we bury it. Even Peter, after he had declared his love and received his commission and even been told in what manner he was to die, could not resist pointing to John and asking, "And what's *he* going to do?" God must feel strongly on the subject for it was one of the few times that Christ was really blunt. His tone of voice may not have been, but the words certainly were. He silenced Peter with one question. "If I will that he tarry till I come, *what is that to thee? follow thou me.*" It was a question to end questions. Peter decided to keep quiet, doubtless being sorry he'd had the crass effrontery to ask. God is the same today, and would deal with us in the same manner. He admonishes us not to diagnose the other fellow's spiritual life, and says, "You follow *me*."

And so we follow Him. We give him all of ourselves, and unconditional surrender always means death to the power of the capitulating army. What we give depends upon what we *are*. What He may allow another, He may not allow us; what He takes from us, He may not have to take from another. From time to time our course may change; if we are wholly His it is not a mistake but another steppingstone in the complete plan. And from time to time He gives us someone to lean on and look up to — and when we are ready for it the crutch is gently removed, and if we cling, forcibly removed. And we stand alone again until we can say with the psalmist: "Whom have I in heaven but thee? and there *is* none upon earth that I desire." What the other fellow is doing or plans to do is not our business, for "we're *us*" and "he's *him*," and the unfathomable depths of us and of him are known only to God. We have the *inclination* to analyze and prescribe. He has both the power and prerogative.

CHAPTER 8

TIME MARCHES ON

Six years—six little years—six drops of time!
. . . Matthew Arnold, Mycerinus

Old Time the clock-setter, that bald sexton time.
. . . Shakespeare, King John

His golden locks time hath to silver turned;
O time too swift! O swiftness never ceasing!
His youth 'gainst time and age hath ever spurned,
But spurned in vain, youth waneth by encreasing.
. . . George Poole, Sonnet

I have always looked with awe and envy at mothers who had the foresight to write down the cute things their children said. In spite of my fanatical thoroughness in other areas of the upbringing of mine, I have been sadly remiss in this respect. I have never remembered first teeth either, or first words, or first steps. They were of earthshaking importance at the time, but once accomplished, the idea of preserving the memory for posterity never occurred to me. There is no box of baby shoes and locks of hair in my attic either. When Gary had his first haircut, his baby locks landed on the barbershop floor and were swept away, never to be seen again. The same thing happened with Steve's first haircut — and the locks on the barbershop floor that time were golden ringlets. Now any mother who doesn't think to pick up a golden ringlet is singularly lacking in sentiment.

I was equally delinquent in remembering measles, vaccinations, whooping cough and all the rest. My only thought of them at all was to be glad that they were behind us. *When* they got behind us was of great import, which I discovered later when I had to fill out various blanks for schools, camps and doctors. I appalled teachers and office personnel alike when I had to stop and — right on the margin of the blank — figure out their birthdates.

Lest I seem too heartless, my neglect of such

matters was equally true in my own affairs. To fill out a vital statistics blank was always an agonizing process. Taking Regents' exams and even state boards was easier. Remembering the years and dates of personal events was a talent I just did not have — a trait I undoubtedly inherited from my mother. When asked what month she was married, she said, "I really couldn't say without looking it up. But it must have been a winter month. I remember it was snowing." And until I had to get my birth certificate for something at seventeen and saw Ethel Marian Mac Namee, I thought my middle name was Lillian.

Our family just took things as they came, and *when* they came didn't matter after they went. There were too many other things constantly coming to bother about the things that went.

Over a span of a few short years, children blurt out a veritable gold mine of gems — some of them are just plain hilarious and some of them contain the wisdom of sages. If we could come out now with half the gems that we uttered while children, all of us would be philosophers, experts in logic, and "funny men." It is a pity that such a vast wealth of material goes down the drain, lost to humanity forever.

Although I hardly ever wrote anything down to save, I did manage spasmodically to save things that were already written. Most of them got lost in too-frequent moving, but a few popped up in an old file a few months ago!

> Dere mother,
> Try to com on parints day.
> Dont com before that becas
> your not aloud to com untill
> we get agusted.
>
> > Gary and Steve

> Dere mother,
> Camp is O K eksep I hav got
> poysin ive and we have to
> march al the tim.
> > Lov
> > Steve

(A composition)
> Last nit we went to a bankuet, and
> it was prity good. Doktor Green spok
> and he spok good but he spok to long.
> Steve toked to laud and mother had to
> tak him out. We had ice creem and cack
> and boy it was good.

(Notes pinned to my door)
Dere mom,
We lik you but somtims your meen.
>Your loving sons.

PS: Your meen a lot.
Dere mom,
You are the best storey teler
in the hole wurld.

>Your boys.

The reason why most of us don't keep records of our children's verbosity and high jinks is that we are sure we are going to remember them. But events crowd in and they get relegated to the deepfreeze of our unconscious and are often lost forever. If we get old enough to get real senile, they are apt to get spewed up again, for a characteristic of senility is no memory at all for recent events, and an uncanny recollection of things long past. But this is a risky thing to plan on, for by that time it is too late to do anything about them, and folks wouldn't listen to us if we did; they are too busy living through events of their own lives *they* won't record.

Time marches on. One moment you are tugging at your mother's sleeve while she is talking to another old lady who she afterwards explains is a "girl she knows in church," and the next moment your children are tugging at your sleeve while you chat with a girl you know in church, who they afterwards snort is "an old lady." And you don't know where the time went.

In all my life I wrote down only a dozen or so things my children said. Most of them appeared, sooner or later, in stories. Some of them mouldered for years in my files because, cute as they were, it isn't often you can write an entire story around a conversation or a cute remark. Sometimes you can though. One remark will trigger off a spurt of creativity, and an entire story will dangle there in the mind, the pieces falling together in joyous anticipation like old friends rushing to a party — until the whole emerges almost at once and more quickly than you can get it down on paper.

These, of course, are rare moments that every writer wishes would happen more often. The fact that they do not is what makes writing such a slow and painful business.

The script in this chapter is a result of one of those rare moments. Steve came in one day from school and with a great flourish handed me a school Christmas play in which he had a few words of great moment and weighty import. He showed me the place in the book, cleared his throat, and said the lines:

Ha ha. Ho ho. I am Jolly Jump-up.
I am very jolly.

He read the lines like a first grade student reading "Oh see the apple in the tree" and sounded about as jolly as Hamlet while he was deciding whether or not to end it all.

The conversation that ensued — my trying to get a spark of life into the dialogue while he stolidly stuck to his unimaginative guns — ended in a draw. Neither of us would budge and he went off to play, muttering his lines under his breath — *his* way. As stubborn as he'd been, I had to chuckle. I was still chuckling an hour later when I decided that if it was *that* funny I'd better write it down. And as I was doing so I remembered another Christmas when Gary had indignantly refused to sing in the Sunday school program with a "bunch of dumb girls." I had pled, threatened and cajoled. I had reminded him that Steve had been in a school festival play with a bunch of dumb girls.

"Yeah — but he just stood there in a Spanish costume in all his splendor and watched the girls dance like matadors," Gary said.

"Yeah — I just stood there in all my splendor and helped carry off the dead matadors." Steve was no help.

In the end I had persuaded Gary with a quiet little private talk that appealed to his higher senses.

As I thought of these two Christmasses, the story emerged almost at once. The rest of it was fiction,

all there in my mind, ready to capture on paper.
And I called it

* * * * *

THE WEEK BEFORE CHRISTMAS

Dear Mother,

I'm writing this by candlelight, and I don't know when it'll get on its way—we don't know much about what's happening around here —haven't even had our clothes off in days— but anyhow, I'm hoping it'll reach you before Christmas. It's sleeting here, but other than that it doesn't have the remotest resemblance to Christmas. The package you wrote about hasn't caught up with me yet—it wouldn't reach me out here anyhow—but I'll be looking forward to it when we get back. I can't help missing you all something awful right now. I keep thinking about crazy things like clean sheets—and licking frosting bowls.

Mom, is the Christmas tree up yet? Can you smell it all over the house? I always used to know when you'd put it up. The minute I came in the back door I could smell it. I guess you might say I've sorta lost my bearings — thinking about things like that. Guess I need a good talking to! I keep thinking about how Christmas would be at home, with you and Dad and white snow and the fireplace— guess I'm feeling sorry for myself. I have to go now. Boy, I had only a few minutes to dash this off and I've spent most of them complaining. Sorry. Give Dad my love. I've never appreciated you both so much.

Love,
David

Dear David:

I've read your letter over for the hundredth time, it seems. I know it by heart. I could start in the middle and say it toward both ends. All anybody has to do is say, "How's David?" — and I'm off for thirty minutes!

Dad has gone to bed, and I'm up, in his chair by the fireplace. Same old chair I've threatened to throw out for fifteen years. He knows I won't. It's too comfortable — just like a bucket.

It's only a week till Christmas, my dear, and memories are fairly leaping up at me from the fire. Tonight it seems as if my whole life were wrapped up in Christmasses . . . it was on Christmas that I met Dad — and it was on a quiet, white Christmas morning that they laid you in my arms for the first time. I looked up at a starched nurse and blinked at her blurry face until it settled into nice comfortable contours. She was holding a bundle. It was you.

"Mrs. Gray — Mrs. Gray — are you asleep?"

"Uh. I — I must have been. I'm drooling."

"Well close your mouth and open your eyes. And Mrs. Gray — meet your new son!"

"Ohhhhh. Is he — did I — ?"

"He is and you did. He's yours and he's all here, safe and sound. Good looking, too. Two feet — two hands — two nose — no, one nose. Look at him! Here. Squiggle over in bed a bit. I'll put him in alongside you."

"D'you think he'll be all right here alongside — "

"I don't know who he'd be alrighter with. You *had* him. He's *yours*. Here!"

She laid you in my arms then. I looked at you with wonder, as most women look at their first-born. I touched your hand.

"Ohhhh. His hands — they're so *little*. I didn't think he'd be so little. I can't believe he's mine. I can't believe he's *real*."

"He's real, all right," she said. "When you hear him cry you'll know he's real." She started for the door. And stopped. "D'you hear it?" she said. It was caroling, off somewhere—faint but unmistakable. With it came the bittersweet joy of Christmas. My eyes stung and my throat tasted salty. "It's the nurses caroling. They're over in the other wing." For a minute she lost her starchiness. "They'll be over here in a few minutes. Nice welcome." And then, "You can hold him closer than that. He won't bite. He doesn't have any teeth. I looked." She opened the door and started through, then turned back a minute. "Merry Christmas, dear," she said. Then the door hissed shut and we were alone, you and I. I told you it was Christmas and that your name was David and I felt of your little hands and feet and then I cried all over your little fuzzy head . . . your little fuzzy head . . .

It was a few moments of such pure joy that it still has the power to awe me, David. I guess I felt like Hannah. You don't put thoughts like I had into words — but that morning I dedicated you to God.

Oh, darling, you were the cutest, the brightest — well, you were a little stinker too. We had our moments. But the Christmasses seem to be the milestones.

Remember the time you came barging in with a part in the school play?

"Mommie!" you said. "I got a part in the Christmas play at school! You have to come and see it. It's Friday night and I'm — I'm —" you fumbled with the script. "Here's my part.

It's important. You can help me learn it. Here."

"Hmmmm. Which one are you?"

"The part that's got the red marks on it. That's me."

"That's I."

"That's what I said. That's me. I'm — well I'll say my part for you — then you'll get the hang of it." You cleared your throat, struck a pose and began: "Ha ha. Ho ho. I am Jolly Jump-up. Oh, I am very jolly."

You were so wooden, so incredibly bad I couldn't believe it. "Mmmmmm," I said lamely. "Then what? Do you have any more?"

"Sure. Flip the page. On top. Right there where it's marked with red. That's me."

"That's — well, never mind. Go ahead."

"Ha ha. Ho — do I have two ho's or three ho's on the second one?"

This was ridiculous. "Does it matter?"

"Oh sure. Once I have two and once I have three and I don't know which is which. I gotta do it right."

"Well you can laugh your head off the second time," I said dryly. "You have four."

"Oh." You cleared your throat again and squared off. "Ha ha. Ho ho ho ho — "

"What on *earth* are you supposed to be?" I knew I wasn't being diplomatic. But I couldn't help it.

"Oh. I'm a jack-in-the-box. A jolly jack-in-the-box. The kids are all toys, see? Under the tree on the stage. And this girl comes in and sees us and stops and exclaims. You know how girls exclaim." You drew in your breath in a quick little gasp to show me. "And she comes over to us and I'm the first one she touches. She presses my button and flips my lid and I come springing out of my box. And that's when I say — 'Ha ha — '"

"Look — David." I was tactful and serious. "You're a happy jolly jack-in-the-box. Why don't you just come up holding your sides and laughing. Just *laugh*. You know — " and gave off with a department store-Santa Claus laugh: "Ho - ho - ho - ho - I am — "

"Mother, don't louse it all up. It has to be the way it is in the book. H - a, exclamation point, h - a, exclamation point, h - o, exclamatoin point, h - o, exclama — hey, d'you know what Alice is going to be?"

"Who Alice? Alice who — whom? David, you have *me* throwing the king's English all over the kitchen. Who is Alice?"

"Alice — my girl. I told you. She plays first base on our team. Best man we ever had on first base. She can ride a bike with no hands — "

"Is she the one who knocked her brother's front teeth out?"

"Yup. D'you know he can whistle through the gap? Every thing he says with an "s" comes out in a whistle if he wants it to. It's great stuff. He can — "

"I'm afraid to ask. What's dear little Alice going to be?"

"She's going to be an angel. With wings and everything. Gauze ones."

"Oh brother."

"Yup. She's going to have gauze wings. Want to hear me again? Ha ha. Ho ho ho — oops, I gotta go. Alice is waiting for me."

"Is this all you — is this your whole part?"

"Yeah. But don't worry. I can learn it. I got all week to practice. Ha ha — "

You were still muttering "ho ho" as you went out the door.

Oh, David — you practiced that thing all week — I almost lost my mind. And when Friday night came, she pressed your button and flipped your lid and you came springing up — took one look at the PTA and went "Daaaaaaaah." That was the Christmas we realized you weren't going to be a thespian.

Remember the Christmas you came home with the Sunday school play in your pocket? "It's a play," you said. "I'm supposed to be in it. But let's get one thing straight. I'm *not* going to stand up there and sing with all those dumb girls."

"But other boys are singing too," I tried,

199

reasonably. "There aren't just dumb — just girls. You're being silly about it. And it's a lovely song."

"It's a baby song."

"It is *not*. It's a timeless, ageless — "

"It's a baby song."

"It's a timeless, ageless classic — "

"It's a baby song."

"It's a timeless, ageless, classic lullaby — "

"IT'S A BABY SONG. AND I'M NOT GOING TO SING IT. IT'S MY BIRTHDAY. IF A FELLOW CAN'T DO WHAT HE WANTS TO ON HIS BIRTHDAY I DON'T KNOW WHEN ELSE A FELLOW CAN DO WHAT HE WANTS TO DO. IF A FELLOW CAN'T DO WHAT HE WANTS ON HIS BIRTH — "

"Oh, hush." We stared at each other for a moment. "Happy birthday, David, come Christmas," I said at last. "Of *course* Christmas is your birthday. But it's something more important that that." I struggled for the right words. "David — everything God ever said hinges on that day when Jesus was born. It's — it's like the hub of a big wheel. All the other things God said are like spokes coming out from the hub. It's the day the Lord Jesus Christ was born — God's promise of a Saviour was kept on Christmas. Jesus *was* God. Nothing else God ever said in the Bible makes *sense* if it weren't for Christmas. Except for Easter when He rose again — Christmas is — is *it*." I stopped suddenly. I felt I'd said enough for the moment. I didn't want to go past the ending. I turned back to the music.

"And it's a lovely song. It's a timeless, ageless lullaby. Not a baby song at all. Try it.

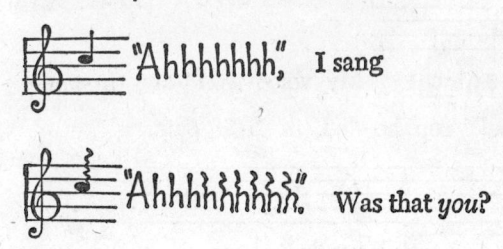

"Ahhhhhhh," I sang

"Ahhhhhhhhhh." Was that *you*?

"Oh brother," I said softly, under my breath.

And again, "Ahhhhhhhhh."

"Ahhhhhh" you struggled valiantly. "Ahhhhhhhhhhhhh—!"

"You've got it—" I sang. "Hang on it—!"

"A-way in a man-ger

"Come-on-David-sing!"

"The lit-tle — My-voice-won't-stay-in-one-place!" You howled, in great pain.

"It doesn't have to"—I sang—"You come right back here! The stars in the sky—It's his-birth-day-first."

"David," I said quietly.

You screwed your face up for an all-out effort. "The lit-tle Lord Je-sus a-sleep on the haaaaay."

202

You were a dreadful singer, David. Your mouth went up sideways when you hit a high note. But that was a special Christmas. That was the Christmas we began saying: "It's His birthday first — "

Remember the Christmas you were almost grown up — but not quite?

"Hi, mom. I'm all set for young people's. We're going to decorate the church for Christmas. How do I look? I've got one of those ties on an elastic — can pull it out and snap it back. See?" You demonstrated and brought it back with a gunnnnnng.

"Don't do that," I said. "It comes back crooked. Let me straighten it up." And then — "David?"

"Hm?"

"Is that all you? Or are you padded?"

"That's all me, Ma'am — all muscle. Wanna see?"

"No — don't take your coat off. You're late. I — just hadn't realized you'd grown so. David — " I looked at you with new eyes, the truth dawning. I was cautious. "Who is she?"

"Who's who? Whom? Who?"

"This woman who has wrought this miraculous change in you. Come now, leave us not quibble. Your neck is clean. And your hair is slicked. And you — hey that's my *Tabu* you have on! I *thought* you smelled familiar!"

"Awww. Just a little. I just got kinda cleaned up. Mom. I'm glad you brought it up. I wanted to talk to you about her. She's sorta — well she's — maybe you know her." You started to describe her with gestures. "She's about this tall — and she's — well she's kinda — she's a little bit like — she's just about this — um — wide, and — " But it was too much. You dissolved sheepishly. "She's a girl." You stopped, spent. I gaped at you foolishly, trying to look interested but not too concerned, as if this happened every day.

"So I gathered," I said dryly, ever ready with the quick answer. I was immediately sorry. Your eyes were begging me not to laugh.

"I got her something for Christmas," you said, glad to change the subject. "I've wanted to talk to you about that too. I don't know whether or not it's okay. I mean if it's not okay — I don't want to get her something that's not okay — you know, if it's not okay — I wouldn't want to give her — if it's not okay — I'll give it to you."

"What is it?" I said, resigned to my lot.

"Perfume. It's good stuff, all right. A whole dollar. Plus tax. Good stuff."

I considered that critically. "Well, it's a lot

better than the plastic dump truck you gave me last year."

Touché for me. You blushed. "Ahhhhh, *Mom*. I was just a *kid* last year. This year — hey can I — d'you suppose — I was wondering if after we decorate tonight, maybe some of the kids could come over here — and we could maybe sing carols or something or hang around and have some popcorn balls — could we have some popcorns balls? — and I could bring her over too and you could kinda meet her — could we have some popcorn balls?"

"We can have some popcorn balls," I said, very serious. You were so defenseless, I couldn't smile. It just wouldn't be cricket. "You'd better go on," I said. "You're late."

You started for the door, came back. "Mom— this is going to be the best Christmas I ever had."

"Yes. Go on. You're late."

"Mom — you'll like her." You laughed foolishly.

"Go *on*!"

You went then, slamming the door, and I was alone and free to laugh. But somehow it was suddenly more poignant than funny.

I did like her. She was all clean and shining. She was your first girl. And you brought her home. Oh, David, that was a *good* Christmas.

Remember the Christmas you came home with something on your mind to tell Dad and me and something to tell your best girl? I met you at the station. You were so tall I saw you right away. I was so short I had a dreadful time getting through the crowd.

"David — David! *Oh I BEG your pardon —I'm all elbows. I'm meeting my son. David! He's over there — the tall one. Merry Christmas!* Oh David!" You gathered me in.

"Merry Christmas, baby."

"Oh, David. Honestly!"

"You look wonderful — where's Dad?"

"Oh, I don't know. I threw a coat over my house dress. Dad's doing some last minute things that came up. We're going to trim the tree tonight. Come on over this way — I'm parked in a limited zone. David, I wasn't going to cry, but I'm so glad you're home. Come on."

"Mom, I've got a lot of things to talk over with you and Dad. I — I changed my course at school. Mom, I — I'm going into Christian service — might want to go on to seminary. I'm not sure. D'you think Dad'll mind? My changing my course? Hey, what's the matter?"

"David I — that's wonderful. This is an *awful* place to break news like that. Let's get out of here. Over this way."

I took your hand and we both talked all the way to the car. David, I wanted to get right down on my knees and thank God for you, right there in the station. But instead I talked about the most ordinary things. It's strange how you dream of the great moments, and then you talk about ordinary things when the great moments come.

Oh, David, that *was* a Christmas. If all the rest of my life nothing wonderful ever happens to me again, I'll still always thank God for that Christmas. You were home — we were all together. And we all said, "Happy birthday, David." And we all thought, "It's His birthday first." It was in us by then, a part of us. We said it every year. But this year was somehow different. This year, when you went back to college —

But you never did go back to college. And now, incredibly, another year has rolled around and it's a week before Christmas again — and you are somewhere overseas and I'm not sure where you are. And I don't know what to write.

David — people change and the world changes and the bottom drops out of your life — but God does not change. Jesus Christ is the same — yesterday, today and forever. Remember what we learned in Romans? That nothing can separate us from the love of God? Neither height nor depth nor famine nor peril — nor war.

David, I'm going to remind you of something and from where you are, it may seem hard. I'm going to remind you again that it's still His birthday first. And I'm going to commit you to Him Who loved you and gave Himself for you and knows where you are. He put you there. If ever I needed to believe these things, I need to believe them now.

So I'm going to wish you a blessed Christmas. For His sake.

Good night, my beloved —
Mother

* * * * *

Yes, time marches inexorably on, and the pity of it is, we do not know it until so much of it has gone. When I wrote the end of that story it was pure fiction, and such stark reality was so far away — beyond the pale of my experience. And we wasted years taking each other for granted, getting enmeshed in the humdrum sameness of things — until quickly — too quickly — the bathos of propinquity turned into the pathos of separation — and the fictitious end of the story was all too real. Before I knew where the years had gone, or even that they were going, Gary was waiting in the car while Steve and I said good-by in the living room because he was adamant about not wanting me to go to the station. "It's rough enough doing it here," he'd said. "Let's not make it worse."

In his army uniform he did not seem at all like Steve, and yet more endearingly like Steve than ever. I prayed aloud for him then, and it was brief, for I did not want to cry. Then, "You know me," he said. "I can't stand good-bys. So let's have it just like I was coming home tonight." His eyes were suspiciously moist, and he turned quickly and ran to the car.

After a moment Gary got out of the car and came back to the living room, his arms out. "I knew you two idiots wouldn't cry in front of each other," he said. "I came back so you could cry on me."

I did.

I told him not to tell Steve I was crying and he said Steve had told him not to tell me how sunk *he* felt and we chuckled through our tears in loving conspiracy. A moment later they disappeared in the traffic. And I wept, not only because he was gone, but for every moment I had not appreciated him while he was here.

There are many illusions in life that trip us up, but one of the most deadly ones is that time is going to stand still while we get straightened out or drop that habit or write that note or do that job or change that attitude or mend that friendship or appreciate that blessing or that person or pay that vow to God.

"Redeem the time," urged Paul. It means literally, "buy up the time" — buy up every moment as investors buy up assets that are going to yield rich dividends in the future. For every moment you buy up and use profitably, you will reap reward. For every moment you use unprofitably, you will reap regret.

Life is only half-filled by untold millions who meant to do something and never got around to it. The lament of them all would fill the world with one great sigh.

There was the man who had a great talent and he dipped into alcohol and first it gave a pleasure and then it had a grip of iron and he kept meaning to do something about it but time went on and after awhile his wife was gone and his children were gone and his job was gone and the great talent was gone and there was nothing left at all but despair — and the tragedy is that all his life he meant to get straightened out.

And the one who wanted to make money but soon money became an obsession and before he knew it his life had gone and though he had always meant to spend time with his wife and children, when he finally got around to it they were strangers who didn't have time for *him*.

And the woman who always meant to spend more time with her widowed mother but when she finally *had* time her mother was gone.

And the man who vowed a portion of his wealth to God and God had prospered him in business and he always meant to tithe but before he knew it death had caught up with him and he'd even forgotten to take care of it in his will.

And the man who was called into full time service and vowed he'd go after he got his affairs straightened out but he never had time — and death caught up with him too before he got around to it.

I read a story once of a hard-working farm woman who lived her life in quiet, uncomplaining stoicism — unappreciated and unsung. She died at the end, as quietly and uncomplaining as she had lived. And when her husband looked down at her gnarled hands and work-worn face, all the sadness and regret of the ages was in his eyes. "I never told her I loved her," he said.

Each of our lives is ordered in a different fashion and it doesn't matter much what God gave us to do. It may be something great and it may be something quite ordinary. The point is, He gave us just so much time in which to do it and time won't wait. Opportunities are snatched by other people, and love dies of neglect and people wither from lack of appreciation and talents peter out from lack of use and children grow up and go away and at the end of our lives we say, "I don't know where the time went."

We'll say it anyway, whether or not we used it well. But how much better to say it knowing that, to the best of our ability, we have "bought it up." Even apparent failure loses its sting in the face of this.

EPILOGUE...

I thought of it again the other day. It was while I was visiting Mike (grandchild #2).

"Mike," I thought, "at a year and a half you really should be saying something else besides gibberish." So I pointed to Marianne and said, "Mom - ee. MOM - EEE."

He just grinned. Well I suppose I did look somewhat foolish. But I persisted. "Mom - ee," periodically during the next hour, and right up until we went to the supermarket.

It was there, when Marianne left Mike with me, took a basket and swished around a corner out of sight, that I got the jolt.

Mike let go of my hand, ran up to where she'd disappeared and shouted up the aisle — "Marianne! MARIANNNNNNE!"

"She'll be back in a minute," I said weakly, very embarrassed.

"Oh," he said. And he trotted back to me matter-of-factly and took my hand again.

Yes, time is still going on, inexorably. And God is so good, so good. Like in the spiritual, *sometimes it causes me to tremble* . . .